The Priceless Cats

AND OTHER ITALIAN FOLK STORIES

Collections of Other Folk Stories by
M. A. JAGENDORF

THE MARVELOUS ADVENTURES OF
JOHNNY DARLING
Stories of the farmer folk hero

NEW ENGLAND BEAN-POT
Folk Stories of New England

UPSTATE, DOWNSTATE
Folk Stories of the Middle Atlantic States

SAND IN THE BAG
Folk Stories of Ohio, Indiana, and Illinois

TYLL ULENSPIEGEL'S MERRY PRANKS
Folk Stories of the Flemish folk hero

THE MERRY MEN OF GOTHAM
The famous folk tales of England

THE GYPSIES' FIDDLE AND OTHER
GYPSY TALES
(in collaboration with C. H. Tillhagen)
Gypsy folk stories

illustrations by
GIOIA FIAMENGHI

New York, The Vanguard Press

THE
PRICELESS
CATS

AND OTHER
ITALIAN FOLK STORIES
by M. A. Jagendorf

To Vittorio Emanuele Guerrini

A SCHOLAR AND A GENTLEMAN
WHO LOVED ITALY AND KNEW ITS TALES

Contents

Preface

Ever since poetry has been sung in words we enjoy even today, Italy has been a great inspiration for poets. The world has never stopped to wonder at, and to enjoy, the infinite beauty of nature and the richness of art of this golden land.

The greatest painters in the world were inspired by its rainbow-colored landscapes, and the most wonderful sculptors ever known created dreams in marble that are an inspiration to this day. Because of this great beauty of Italy, men have been, and still are, drawn to it. And I, too, have gone there again and again to

9

be refreshed by its delightful enchantment and beauty and warmth.

Beginning with 1931, I went there almost every year, for I wanted to write yet another book about the most perfect human being of the last two thousand years: Francis of Assisi.

During my stays in Italy I heard stories that I loved —stories of wonder and stories of adventure; tales of wisdom and tales of laughter. I enjoyed these so much that I wanted others to share my pleasure, so I decided to put them into a book.

About that same time I became friends with Miss Flamminia Guerrini, who was born in Italy and lived most of her life in Florence. I asked her to help me, and she, with Miss Lucia Mosiici, also a Florentine, did it with such good will that they might almost be called co-authors.

There was still a third source and inspiration for these folk tales: the city in which I have lived most of my life—New York. Here there are more Italians than in any city outside of Italy, and here I heard many Italian folk stories from those who had migrated from the boot-shaped land of citron blossoms and ancient vineyards.

The stories I have set down here were told to me.

The contributions of Miss Guerrini and Miss Mosiici are tales they heard or read in their younger years in folk-story books, of which there are very many in Italy.

In addition to the pleasure of reading these stories of rich adventure, you will also learn in them some interesting facts about the different customs and beliefs of the Italian people.

The religious tales indicate how deep-rooted a part religion plays in the Italians' daily life. And they show the close, friendly way in which the people think of the Lord and His teachings.

Some of these tales also show the often unusual attitude of Italian people toward sorcery and magic. Magic for them is not quite a "black art," with the horror found in the legends of some other lands. In Italy sorcery often can be put to good use and wise help. The woman who knows magic uses it to help instead of to hurt.

Again, these tales show how Italian folk live, think, and act. "Eat and Like It" tells you that polenta— corn meal—was (and still is) used in many forms and was the daily food of many people—and tells what they thought of it! Sometimes the wisdom of a good priest was needed to teach them to like it.

In *"A Lesson Well Learned"* and in the *"Giufa"* stories the wise thoughts of Italians are disclosed. In *"The Lucky Dog"* and in some of the others you will learn of folk beliefs and faiths. Each story is an expression of the Italian way of life. Folk stories such as these reveal the history of the Italian people even more than battles and conquests do, for the stories express the dreams and hopes and life of a nation.

These tales are just a few green blades in the rich field of folk stories that are to be found in Italy, and I hope they will give you a desire to go more deeply into the subject, both for pleasure and study.

M. J.

The Priceless Cats

AND OTHER ITALIAN FOLK STORIES

Fish Alive!

In the region of Tuscany in the central part of Italy there is the beautiful city of Siena. It is called the City of Dreams because it is full of lovely churches, fine palaces, and magnificent paintings. In the olden, golden days, artists were honored there like princes. Any boy who could draw was apprenticed to some artist, in the hope that he, too, would become a craftsman of beauty.

Now, there lived near that proud city a poor peasant boy, Domenico by name, who, from the day he could hold charcoal in his fingers, loved to draw. And soon he learned to make likenesses of everything around him: the pots in his mother's kitchen; the chickens, goats, dogs, pigs, cats, horses on the farm—anything he saw. A nobleman named Lorenzo Beccafumi noticed this, and with the parents' consent took the boy to Siena to be apprenticed to a painter.

Domenico had a wonderful time in the city. He drew everything he saw. The rest of the time he played about the weaving, narrow streets and creepy corners with boys his own age. His friends called him Mecherino, which means "little Domenico," and there wasn't anyone who could beat him at playing games or tricks.

But one day the playing came to an end. His noble foster father apprenticed him to a famous painter. There, in addition to lessons in drawing and painting, he had to clean brushes and pans, run errands, and do all kinds of work.

The great painter was a hard taskmaster, and the boy never had a free minute. No sooner were the lessons done than it was: "Mecherino, do this; Mecherino, do that. Wash the pots; run for sausages; get vegetables; go and buy fish; get nuts."

"Why can't I play with my friends?" Mecherino would ask.

"If you want to become a famous painter of Siena, you must forget childish games."

But Mecherino was young and loved playing as much as he loved painting. He could not understand why a boy could not be a good painter and have fun as well. Day and night he racked his brain to prove this to his master.

One day his master sent him to buy fish. He carried a brown basket on his arm and ran like a scuttling mouse to the market place. There the clangorous crowd in rainbow colors was a joy to behold—most of all by Mecherino, who had the eye of an artist.

Folks were dressed in every shade of smock and hosen: yellow and black, green and blue, white and purple. Ladies wore puffed sleeves and bright-hued kirtles. Peasants and merchants showed their bright, jangling wares temptingly.

Mecherino, pushing this way and that, spied a mess of glistening blue and coral fish lying on round green leaves. He sat down on the ground, put his basket next to him, and began bargaining with the fishman. While they were higgling and haggling about the price, a young redheaded rapscallion, on whom Mecherino had played many a trick, crept up and pulled apart the wickers at the bottom of the basket, so that anything put into it would fall out. Then the mischievous rascal ran off into the milling crowd.

The bargaining ended, the fishmonger threw some round green leaves into Mecherino's basket, put in five slithery fish, and covered them with a few more leaves. Neither he nor the boy saw the open spaces at the bottom. Now Mecherino eagerly joined the jostling crowd, shouting, laughing, pinching, and never noticing that the fish were falling out one after the other. When he reached home, his master took the basket and looked into it—it was empty!

You can just imagine the scolding and trouncing Mecherino got. Words and blows thudded on him like hard apples dropping from a tree on a windy day.

"You knave! I have all this trouble with you because you are play-crazy. You will never be a painter, I can tell you that. Never!"

Mecherino was silent. What could he say? From then on it was worse than before. He was kept busy from the rising of the sun to the fading of the stars. He never had a free minute.

Came another day when he was sent to buy fish, for his master liked fish more than meat.

This time Mecherino was very careful and watched his basket anxiously. On the way home he looked in it a dozen times to make sure nothing had fallen out. When he arrived he took the fish upstairs into the kitchen and then went down into the workroom.

Now, Mecherino had as lively a mind as he had a clever hand; he could think of a good jest as well as make a good drawing. For weeks his mind had been spinning around and around trying to weave an idea to prove that he could work as well as he could paint. He was sure that if he could please his master in both, he would not have to work so hard and he would get a little free time to romp around. Suddenly a thought, bright as a sunbeam, shot through his mind. He'd show his master that he could work well and play, too—by a jest! And no lesson is so easily learned as through a jest.

Quickly he fetched his paint and brushes and began painting fishes all over the stone stairs that led from the street entrance to the floor above, where the kitchen was. He painted these fishes on different steps, lying in all kinds of positions. He used the loveliest glistening blues, corals, and pale yellows, and when he was finished the fish looked as if they had just been taken from the cold green water and flung all over the stairs. Truly, you would swear they were alive!

The paint dried quickly because he had put a good deal of drier into it.

He looked at his work with a happy smile and then went outside the great, dark chestnut door of the house and sat down to wait. In good time his master returned. No sooner did he see Mecherino sitting idly in the doorway than he began shouting harshly.

"There you are, lolling at the door, wasting golden hours. Why aren't you at work? Did you bring the fish or did you lose them on the way as you always do?"

"I brought them home, master, and you can see them at once. Just step in."

The master stepped inside. No sooner did he see the seemingly live fish lying all over the stairs than he began screaming loud enough to be heard at the end of the town.

"Varlet! Good-for-naught! Why are these fish lying all over the stairs to rot when they should be in

the kitchen in cool water? By the saints! They must all be spoiled. I'll pay you for this. Quick, pick them up or the stick'll be dancing on your back!"

"I can't. I am sorry, I can't," said Mecherino, head down and trying to hide his laughter.

The master painter, too angry to hear the boy, bent down to pick up the beautifully glistening fish —and then felt and saw that they were painted!

He stood up, eyes and mouth open in surprise; then he said slowly, "Who painted these beautiful fish?"

"I did, master," Mecherino said meekly.

"You did?"

"Yes, I did. I wanted to show you that I can paint and do my work, too. Can't I have a little time, master . . . to be with my friends?"

The master did not say anything, but from then on Mecherino did have free time to play with his friends through the narrow cobbled streets of the City of Dreams.

Domenico di Pace (which was his peasant father's name) Beccafumi became a great artist and an ornament to his city. He painted many, many religious pictures in churches and palaces, and he was also a clever engineer. When Emperor Charles V came to Siena, Mecherino constructed a tremendous arch and a marvelous mechanical horse.

His greatest work of art is a mosaic design in the pavement of the cathedral of Siena showing many scenes from the Bible. The work is as ingenious as it is beautiful, and it took Mecherino many years to do it. To this very day it is one of the wonderful sights of Siena, and people from all over the world come to see it.

The Miracle of the Rose

Long, long ago there lived in Piedmont—a region in northern Italy that is rich with royal palaces and feudal castles—a countess named Paula. She was as beautiful as she was kind, and she always helped the sick and the poor. Her heart was so full of loving goodness that she wanted everyone in the world to be happy, and for that reason she was ever giving charity to those in need. But alas! She could not do as much as she would have liked to do. The man she loved most, her husband, was hard and haughty, as well as greedy and uncharitable. He looked with disapproving eyes on his wife's kind deeds and often forbade her to give anything to the poor—even a smile or a good word. And he was always on the watch to see if she obeyed his orders.

The lovely countess tried in every way to teach her husband the virtue of golden generosity. She pleaded and sometimes she even cried, but neither tears nor pleas were of any help. The count's heart was stony cold and could not be softened.

"Stop giving food and clothes to the poor, or soon we'll be one of them ourselves," was always his cry. This made the countess sad, but it did not stop her charity.

The count soon knew this, so he put the bread and meat, the wine and cheese under heavy locks and bars. Poor Lady Paula was grieved to tears. She prayed to the good Lord to help her in her plight, for she could not see suffering and stand by without helping.

One day, after praying long and lovingly, she accidentally touched a locked door, and, lo! a miracle! The door opened as if it had no lock at all! The countess was as overjoyed as if Heaven had opened. Behind that door were bread and cheese and other good things to eat. She filled her apron and gave the food to those in need. Then she came back for more, and there was another miracle! The shelves from which she had taken the good food were full again, as if nothing had been taken from them! From then on the same wonderful miracles continued. Every locked door was opened by her touch, and every shelf was full, no matter how much she took from it. The countess and the poor truly led a life of roses in the sunshine.

Now, the count noted this quickly enough and could not figure out what was happening. His wife did not plead with him, and the poor seemed happy, yet nothing was missing from his shelves and bins. He racked his mind to try to understand this, but he saw no light, and suspicion was gnawing him like worms in wood. So he kept constant watch over his wife.

One day he was standing at the foot of the grand stairway of his castle behind a round stone pillar when Countess Paula came out of the pantry, her apron bulging high with freshly baked breads. The count's eyes glittered sharply. "Now I have caught her. What is she carrying from the pantry all covered up in her apron?" he thought.

"Madam," he said harshly, "pray tell me, what is in your apron that you have closed so carefully?"

Countess Paula stopped on the steps, but she was not afraid. She knew the Lord would take care of her. A warm smile lit her lovely face.

"My lord," she said graciously, "I carry in my apron things sweet-scented and lovely to look at, which make people happy and contented. I carry in my apron sweet, fresh . . . different kinds of roses."

Now, the count, though a harsh and close-fisted man, was also polite, as a count should be. He did not believe his wife's words, but he bowed low and said:

"If you have so many roses in your apron bulging like a cloud, may I not have one to wear in my berrettone as a favor? Come, let me pick one." He came right up to her, pulled open the apron, expecting to find food taken from the pantry, and saw instead— an apron full of pale yellow roses! He stood stone silent, not able to move or speak. The countess gracefuly took a yellow rose with a long green stem and gave it to her husband. He took it, put it in his berrettone beside a purple plume, and went off, saying only, "Thanks, my lady."

No sooner was he gone than Countess Paula again felt the weight of the bread in her apron. Smiling happily, she sent a perfumed prayer to the Lord in Heaven and turned to her errand of mercy.

The count went into the courtyard to watch his masons and retainers repair the stones around the moat. And as he stood watching them he noted the men turning from him, trying to hide smiles on their faces. One fellow with straw for brains guffawed loudly, pointing to the count's berrettone. The noble gentleman grew red with anger.

"Oaf! Varlet! Lout!" he roared. "Art laughing at me?"

"My lord," the captain said, "my lord! You have a strange thing on your headgear, and you must not blame the fool too much."

Now the count felt something heavy on his berrettone. Taking it off his head, he saw—a loaf of bread beside the purple plume, not the pale yellow rose he had put there!

For a long time he stood, saying nothing but thinking hard. He was a sharp man and understood quickly why the bread had changed to roses in his wife's apron, and why the rose had changed to bread on his berrettone.

From that day on there was a miraculous change in the count's heart. Cruelty became kindness;

greediness, generosity. It was not long before he joined his wife in her godly work, helping those in need. And the Lord blessed them in all their ways for the rest of their lives.

King Clothes

It is told that years ago there lived in Sicily, the largest island in all the Mediterranean, a young fellow named Giufa, who was so silly that, as the saying goes, he wasn't sure of the weather when it was raining in buckets. That is what folks said, but I'm not sure they were right. For people lived in Sicily before they lived anywhere in Italy, and there must have been silly fellows before him.

Giufa wore rags for clothes and never had shoes, so the dust on the road jumped between his toes. And who looks at a fellow who is dressed in rags? Nobody. Doors were closed in his face, and sometimes people wouldn't ever talk to him. He was never asked to a wedding or a feast. Life was not too pleasant for Giufa.

One sunny day his mother sent him to take something to the farm that was next to theirs.

Giufa went off whistling, kicking the dust on the road. Sometimes he stopped to speak to a bird or a butterfly. Soon he came to the farmhouse. At the gate stood the wife of the farmer.

"Good day, mistress," Giufa said politely. "My mother sent me to give you this," and he held out a basket to her.

The woman took one look at his ragged clothes and dusty face and feet.

"Drop it right there," she cried, "and go quickly. You look like a scarecrow, and the dogs will be after you."

Giufa did not say anything. What could he say? Besides, it was dinnertime just then, and his stomach was empty and growling. So he turned sadly toward home.

Though kith and kin said he was a noodlehead, he had sense enough to think that the farmwoman could have been a little nicer and could have asked him in to have a piece of bread and cheese.

When he reached home he told his mother how

he had been treated, adding: "I could smell the bean soup out at the gate. They could have been good Christians and asked me to have a plate. They talk to me like that because I don't wear fine breeches and a velvet coat."

Giufa's mother worried about this, and a few weeks later she once again had to send her son with something to that same farm. Not wanting to put the boy to shame, she dressed him in a fine white shirt, good breeches, a nice blue coat, and good shoes.

You should have seen Giufa! He looked like a different fellow. He almost could not recognize himself.

Off he went, whistling gaily and joking with bird and beast until he came to the farmer's house. There stood both the farmer and his wife, and neither one recognized Giufa in his fine clean clothes.

"I have something for you," he cried.

It was noon then, and so they greeted him pleasantly and invited him into the farmhouse. They asked him to sit down to hot steaming minestrone soup that was filled with fresh vegetables and good sharp cheese. With it came crisp fresh bread and rich red wine.

Giufa ate and joked and had the best time of his life. At the end of the meal, the farmer sat back and asked the boy to tell him about this and that. But instead of doing so, Giufa stood up and put some of the cheese and bread in the pockets of his coat and breeches and into his hat. The farmer and his wife laughed because they thought this was so funny. Then Giufa bowed low and, looking down at his bulging pockets and over at his hat, said:

"Here is food for you, my good clothes and fine hat, and I want to thank you from the bottom of my heart, for it is you who were treated like a king, and it is because of you, my good clothes and fine hat, that I had a fine meal. When I came here the last time without you, fine clothes, I was treated like a crazy dog."

Then he turned around and walked out. You can guess what the farmer and his wife thought and said! Maybe they remembered the saying: "Dress up a stick and folks'll think it's a nobleman."

The Lucky Dog

Once there lived in Piedmont a man by the name of Giovanni who had a large family but little money. He was a daydreamer and always imagined he would find great fortunes that would allow him and his family to have all the things in the world they wanted. His head was just brimful of jingling treasures.

Sometimes he tried to help his dreams a little. On warm nights, when fireflies sparkled in the dark, he would dig in the ground looking for gold in the black earth. He knew that in far-off days, in those very fields where he worked, there had stood the great and powerful city of Pollentia, with a magnificent royal palace. Folks said that when the Germans had come long before to destroy and kill, many Italians had buried their gold and jewels in the earth. That was the gold for which he was searching. If only he could find one of those buried treasures! In the warm evenings, when golden stars spotted the sky, he would dig in the ground looking for gold in the thickset earth.

One night, when the wind was murmuring around his home, he had a dream. He dreamed his old father stood before him and said, "Son, you are always thinking about finding treasures."

"That I am, Father."

"Then, my son, go to the bridge of Pavia, where you will find that for which you are looking."

The next morning, when the dew was still glistening, Giovanni said good-by to his wife and children, took some cheese and bread in his bag, and set off to the bridge of Pavia on the Ticino River.

It did not take him too long to reach that famous bridge, which folks said was built in a single night by the Devil himself. But that is another story.

He sat down on the bridge and waited for the

treasure to come to him, as his father had said it would.

One day: nothing happened—no treasure. Folks passed on foot, with horses, or with oxen. Some looked at him, others did not. A few greeted him.

Another day: the same over again. A third day: the same.

One driver with a cart drawn by oxen had passed him every day, and the driver and Giovanni had spoken a few words with each other. On the third day the driver said to him, "Friend, you sit here day after day. Today you look angry. Why do you sit here, and why do you look angry?"

Giovanni just had to speak to somebody, so he told him his story. And he told him about his dream, too, and said he was waiting for the dream to come true.

The driver listened and then he said:

"My dear fellow, I see you believe in dreams. I don't. I think they are just like clouds in the sky. No matter what my dreams are, I never bother about them. Why, a few nights ago I dreamed that in a field where the old city of Pollentia stood there was a stone dog that had a treasure in it. Do you think

I believe in such an old woman's tale? Not me. Take my advice and go home to your wife and children and be satisfied with what you have. That's the way to look on life. May luck go with you."

Then he flipped the brown twig in his hand and the white oxen lumbered on.

Giovanni jumped to his feet and forgot even to say good day to the driver. He remembered that he had seen a stone dog in a ditch in a field in which he had been working. It was a large dog, all beaten and battered.

He ran all the way home and, without even talking to his wife and children, took his heavy stone mallet and rushed to the field and to the ditch. Sure enough, there lay that old stone dog. One ear was missing, and his nose was broken off.

Bang! The mallet struck the stone, then again and again, until the stone split open, and there, wonder of wonders, were seven little gold dogs made many, many years before and hidden away from the robbing German invaders! Giovanni danced with joy and shouted:

"Father, you were right, and dreams do come true!"

He sold the gold dogs one by one, and they

brought him so much money that he and his family had all they wanted for the rest of their lives.

So you see, some people catch fish even when they are asleep. Or, better still: *Vale più un'oncia di fortune che una libbra di sapere,* which simply means: one ounce of good luck is worth endless pounds of knowledge.

Chirola and
the Black Old Man

In the days of bold knights and poor peasants, there lived a man by the name of Chirola near the famous Abbey of Vallombrosa, which is on a mountain about twenty miles from the glorious city of Florence. Though he was a good worker, and honest, he was a hard man who used ungodly language most of the time. He had a black temper and was forever quarreling with his friends and even with his close relatives.

Chirola had a younger brother who was just the opposite. Agnolo (that was his name) was kind and loving and forever doing good. He was betrothed to a sweet girl by the name of Ildegarda, and they were very happy, for soon they were to be married. This made Chirola furious, for, he said, his younger brother—"the good-for-nothing," he called him— was spending his time with his bride instead of working in the fields. And this meant *he* had to work that much harder.

Late one afternoon Chirola was mowing wheat all alone. He was in an ugly mood, and swearing at all the world at the very top of his voice. At the end, when he was angrier than a hive of angry bees, he cried out:

"I'm so mad, if the Devil himself should jump out of the earth I'd make mincemeat of him."

No sooner were the words out of his mouth than there sat before him a black little old ugly man grinning from ear to ear.

"What are you doing in my field, you black imp?" cried Chirola. "You won't get a grain of wheat from me, even if you are the Devil himself. Get out of my way or I'll throw my scythe at you."

The old man did not answer. He just got up and disappeared.

The next day Chirola rose betimes to go to the fair at Vallombrosa to sell a pair of oxen. He was

41

dressed in rags, whereas other folks, going the same way, were dressed in holiday clothes and were of good cheer.

At the fair he asked far more for his oxen than they were worth, for Chirola was the kind who would get blood out of a turnip. No one would buy the animals from him, and he turned home cursing, hungry, tired, and without a kind word or thought for anything living.

Soon the oxen stopped, and Chirola saw in the road the same little ugly man he had seen before. On his arm he had a basket of ripe figs.

Without saying a word, Chirola began gobbling the figs in the basket.

"Now pay me for the figs," the little man croaked.

"Ha, ha, ha," Chirola laughed. "I didn't say I would pay you. The joke is on you. You should have made an agreement first. Now it's a little late. Get out of my way, or I'll give you a beating besides."

The little old man just laughed and disappeared.

Some weeks later, the wedding of Agnolo and Ildegarda was to take place, and Chirola had to go to the bride's home to get the wedding gifts. There were twelve pairs of sheets, thirty towels, fifteen dresses, the bridegroom's shirt—beautifully embroidered by the bride—and many other fine things.

Chirola came early in the morning. He entered the bride's home with a scowling face, scarcely even greeting anyone. Ildegarda's parents were hurt by this, but they did not say a word. They just packed all the things in the lovely painted wooden wedding chest while Chirola grumbled all the time. Then he left, slamming the gate because they had offered him no food. He never thought they might be too frightened by him to offer him anything.

He rode off, swearing as usual, and stopped at the first inn he saw. Leaving the horses and wagon outside, he went in.

When he came out—wagon and horses were gone!

"Those accursed animals went home, leaving me to trudge back on foot. May the Devil swallow them! But here are the tracks of the wheels, and I think I can hear the bells on the harness. I'll catch them and teach them a lesson with the whip they won't forget." He began running after the sound of the bells. He ran and he ran, but no matter how fast he went he couldn't catch up with those jingling bells and crunching wheels. He could hear the noise, but neither horses nor wagon ever came in sight. They seemed to be just in the air. He ran faster and faster and became more and more furious, but nothing helped. There was only the jingling of bells and the crunching of wheels, and nothing in sight except himself, running and panting.

Night came, and morning followed, and Chirola was still running. His breath came like a whistle and his chest ached, but he could not stop running after that ghost wagon. His legs seemed to move without his will. Something was pushing him all the time.

The wedding day came, but Agnolo and Ildegarda could not be married, for the wedding gifts and Chirola were gone, no one knew where. They did not know he was running after those ghost horses and wagon.

Chirola's eyes were red and his chest heaved and then, all of a sudden, the jingling of the bells and crunching of the wheels stopped, and there the cart was—right in front of him! He leaped on the seat and saw, sitting on the bridal chest, a coal-black goat. With all his strength he picked up the goat and threw it on the road. Then he whipped the horses fiercely. They took a few steps and stopped suddenly. In the middle of the road was the little old ugly man he had seen in the wheat field and with the figs.

"Out of my way, you damned beast," Chirola screamed, "or I'll run you down."

The little old man laughed, showing his white pointed teeth, and began running zigzag in the road right in front of the horses. The horses followed him, dragging and bumping and banging the cart and Chirola.

First Chirola crouched down in the seat so as not to fall out. Then, when he saw no end to the game, he leaped out onto the black fellow's back.

A terrible battle began between the two. First one was on top, then the other. They rolled on the ground between the horses' legs and between the wheels.

The battle went on; now Chirola was on top, pushing and pushing the old man—and suddenly he was all alone! Horses and cart were gone, and in his hand was a fiery rod.

He sat a long time without moving, for now he understood that it was the Devil with whom he had been battling. He got up, more dead than alive with fright and weariness, and began to walk homeward.

Ildegarda was sitting sadly in the house when suddenly she cried out with joy, for there, outside the gate, was the cart with the wedding chest and the horses. But there was no sign of wheel tracks on the road—or of Chirola.

Agnolo and Ildegarda were happily married, and a week later Chirola was found in the field where he had first called upon the Devil to appear.

The whole town wanted to know what had happened to him, but you couldn't drag a word out of him with a team of horses. But from then on, no one ever heard him curse again. He was a changed man. As for Agnolo and Ildegarda, they lived happily all their days.

The Priceless Cats

Among the ancient Romans there was a proverb that those who are greedy never have enough, and since the Romans were Italians, the proverb still holds true. In the golden city of Venice they tell a tale that proves this time-old saying.

There lived in that city by the sea two merchants who were neighbors. Both were rich. Both had grand palaces on the green, shimmering canal, with proud gondolas tied to cinnabar-and-yellow-striped poles. And both had lovely young children who were friendly and played with one another. As for the merchants, one was as different from the other as a black pebble from a shining ruby.

One was hard and sharp and greedy, wanting whatever he saw, whether he needed it or not, while the other was generous and good, working to help not only himself but others as well. The two merchants knew each other and spoke to each other, but when it came to business, Mr. Greedy-Wolf was wary and watchful, not trusting anyone—not even himself.

So time went by, with these two buying and selling, working and growing.

Came a day when Giovanni, the good merchant, set out on a far journey to trade for spices, which were much sought after in Europe then.

He loaded his vessels with toys and corals and silks and beautiful glassware to exchange for pepper and cinnamon and vanilla and curries and other scented spices that grew on the islands far away.

He sailed for days and weeks and then came to the rich East, where he traded from island to island, with benefit to himself and satisfaction to the islanders.

One sparkling morning he came to a harbor that was as still as a graveyard, with masts hanging like tombstones. The streets and the markets were quiet as the night.

The merchant and some of his men walked about
—disturbed by their own footsteps. Where were the
hustling and bustling townspeople dressed in color-
ful clothes? Where were the smells of spices and the
cries of vendors that usually filled the air of a busy
city?

Finally the traders from Venice met two men
who took them before the King. The ruler sat on
his throne with a sorrowful face and head bowed
low. Courtiers stood around, no different from the
King.

"Can we trade with your people, Your Majesty?"
the Venetian merchant said. "We have rich goods
from our land that we would gladly exchange for
spices."

"Master merchant," said the ruler, "our spices
are ravaged, our grain is destroyed, our food is
ruined. It is a wonder we are alive, because of the
terrible plague that has come over our land. Everything is slowly being destroyed—even our clothes."

"And what is this terrible plague that has
brought your land such unhappiness, Your Majesty?"

"Gnawing rats and scuttling mice! They are in our
homes and clothes and in our fields and roads. We

49

have set traps for them and we have strewn poison in the pantries, but that has done more harm to our animals than to the pests. There seems to be no remedy for this curse."

"Have you no cats?" the merchant asked.

"Cats? What are cats?"

"Why, cats are furry little animals like small dogs, and they are the mortal enemies of mice and rats, destroying them wherever they find them!"

"Where can I find these cats!" the King cried. "I'll pay anything for them!"

"Your Majesty," Don Giovanni said, "you do not have to pay for cats. We have many of them on our ship, and I will gladly give you a present of some; I am certain your pests will soon be gone."

The King thanked the merchant, almost with tears in his eyes, and within an hour the merchant brought two fine cats—one, a black Tom as fierce as he was big, and the other a lovely tiger-striped lady cat who was famous for having many kittens and catching even more mice.

The King and the islanders looked with awe and wonder at the two animals, for they had never seen cats before, and when they saw them set to work at once on the mice and rats, they were so overjoyed that they wanted to sing and dance.

The King was grateful from the bottom of his heart and wanted to prove this to the merchant, so he showered him and his crew with bales of spices and gleaming jewels, with sweet-smelling sandal-wood and carved ivory, beautiful as a song.

When the merchant and his crew sailed home, they were so happy and contented that even the wind and the waves knew it and led their vessel swiftly back to Venice.

And the joy of Don Giovanni's family was great when he reached home, and great was the excite-ment of his fellow merchants of Venice when they saw his royal cargo.

Don Giovanni met Don Cesare, his neighbor, before the golden church of San Marco, that treas-ury of beauty in the world. They spoke of this and that, about the journey and the trading, and then Don Giovanni told Don Cesare how he had traded the richest merchandise of all for just a pair of common cats. Don Cesare's tongue nearly hung out with greed and envy when they parted.

Thereafter, day and night, Don Cesare could

think only of how Don Giovanni had gained a treasure by giving away two worthless cats that any Venetian would pay to get rid of. He had no peace, and he was more restless than a horse with a thorn in its side. Green jealousy and greed ate into him like fire in dry grass, until he could stand it no longer. He had to go to that island and bring back as big, if not a bigger, treasure than had Don Giovanni.

He fitted out a splendid ship filled with the best of goods, golden vessels, brocades, carved corals. With such gifts the generous King should give him twice—no, three times—as many riches as he had given Don Giovanni.

Soon Don Cesare reached the island. He told the King he was a friend of Don Giovanni. The King received him with open arms, only too happy to welcome a friend of the man who, by his generous gift, had rid the island of the terrible pests.

Don Cesare told the King he, too, had brought him gifts—gifts much more valuable than those of Don Giovanni. Then he presented his gifts of golden cups and carved corals, rich brocades and gilded embroideries—the richest Venice could show—to prove his friendship.

Truly the emperor was overwhelmed by this show

of unselfish generosity. He was a simple and an honest man, and appreciative as well, and he thought hard how he could repay the friendship shown by Don Cesare. Try as he would, he could think of nothing rich enough and fine enough.

In the end he called together his counsellors to decide what to give to Don Cesare in return for the lavish presents, which, the King thought, Don Cesare had given out of the kindness of his heart.

Each elder had his say. In the end, one rich in wisdom arose and said, "Oh, King, this man from Venice has given to you and to us things that will be a joy to look at for years to come. Truly, we in our little island have no gifts to equal his. We could give him spices and perfumes and woods, but these are simple things growing freely in our land. They come and go every year. But there is one thing we possess now that is of great value in this world.

"Not so long ago we were cursed with a pest that nearly destroyed us. The rats and mice overran our land, starved our children, and covered our homes with filth. Then we received a priceless gift that made us once again a free and happy people. Since that time, those precious cat animals have increased in number, and we can well afford to give some of them away, precious as they are to us. I would therefore say to give to Don Cesare, that most unselfish Venetian, two of those invaluable cats. I am sure they will bring to him as great a blessing as they have brought to us."

King and counsellors thought this a splendid and wise suggestion. A cage of solid gold was made, and the King himself chose as the proper gift the two prettiest and most playful kittens that could be found.

Then the King set a day for the great royal audience to present the merchant with his reward. All the counsellors came, and as many people as the room could hold, and then the merchant appeared before the King. He came with light steps and greedy thoughts, thinking of the riches he would reap now—riches that would surely be greater than those Don Giovanni had received.

There were blowing of trumpets and beating of drums and many falderal speeches of friendship on the part of the merchant.

In the end the royal master said, "Don Cesare, you came to our land and gave me kingly gifts freely from the goodness of your heart. That is a fine thing for a man to do. And, as the saying goes, from

seeds of goodness grow rich purple plums of goodness. I and my counsellors thought for a long time how to reward you properly for such unselfish generosity, and finally we decided on the most valuable gift we have.

"When my people and my land were in their greatest distress, a countryman of yours saved us by giving us a gift. It was a gift more precious than gold or diamonds or spices. We have been unable to think of anything more wonderful than the same gift for you. We know it will bring you the same joy and peace it has brought to us. Soldiers, bring the golden cage with the royal gift for Don Cesare!"

Then two soldiers came in with the golden cage in which the two little kittens were playing in a way that was a joy to behold.

The soldiers stopped with the cage before the merchant. The King smiled happily, as did the courtiers and the people.

The merchant looked at the kittens, but he could not say a word, and when he saw everyone beaming and smiling at him, he had to smile, too—a smile that stretched from ear to ear. . . . Soon after he sailed homeward.

Shall I tell you how he felt? Well, I will. The first

few days he was full of fury and hatred, and not a man could speak to him. Then, little by little, he began to see how fate had played a joke on him that he could not change with all his riches and all his power. And, slowly, like the trickle of a single crystal drop of water, he began to think that perhaps jealousy and greed were the wrong seeds for the flowers he wanted in life.

He never said a word to anyone in Venice about what had happened, but it was noticed that he acted more kindly toward people, and that he no longer raced so wildly after gold and riches as he had done before.

The Hand of the Lord

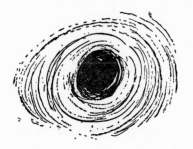

When boys and girls go into the woods around Salerno they look for pine cones. When they find them, they break the kernels of the cones to look for the figure of a hand there. When they see the hand, they believe it is the hand of the Lord. And I will tell you why.

When the Lord Christ walked on the earth, one day He had to flee from enemies into the forest. He ran and He ran, but soon the soldiers were almost upon Him. So what do you think He did? He made himself so small He could creep into a kernel of a pine cone and hide himself in it.

So He hid himself in the kernel of the pine cone, and the soldiers looked for Him all over and could not find Him. In the end they gave up and went back to the city.

When they were gone, the Lord got out of the pine cone, but He was in a hurry and His hand got stuck. He had to pull very hard to get it out. It came out, but it left a mark of His holy hand in the kernel. It was from that time on that you can see the likeness of a hand inside the kernel of a pine cone.

A Long, Long Night

Not far from gay Siena, high on the blue-treed mountains, is a little town called Montieri. In that town live folks who have heavy muscles and light heads, and the people of Siena are ever ready to make sport of the Montierini.

Now, every year there is a great horse race in Siena, in the Piazza del Campo, called *Corsa del Palio,* the course of the banner. The one who wins the race receives a banner.

Riders and horses and a grand procession of boys and men from the different *contrada* (quarters of the town) parade and go through beautiful old ceremonies, to the cheering of the large crowds of people who come there.

One time three of the boldest and most adventuresome men in Montieri decided to go and see that *Palio.*

They started off on foot early in the clear, bell-like morning, and came to Siena just as a great red-balled sun was setting in the west.

Now, the Montierini speak a language a little hard to understand, and they are shy when it comes to conversation with strangers, never getting much farther than "yes" or "no." And even these words they say differently from other Italian folk. Instead of *si,* which means "yes," and *no,* which means "no," they say quickly *"me* si"* for "yes," and *"me no"* for "no." Strangers laugh at them for this, and that makes them even shyer.

In Siena the three Montieri countrymen went to an inn, for they had no friends in the city. After many signs and words they made the innkeeper understand that they wanted to stay to see the *Palio.*

They sat down to a good supper, ate quietly, and were shown to their room for the night.

* In Italian *me* means "me" or "myself." It is pronounced "may."

As is the custom to this day in Italian cities, the wooden shutters of the windows were tightly closed. The three men said their prayers and went to sleep.

Since the day of the *Palio* is a great holiday in Siena, men, wagons, carts, horses, and oxen began passing through the cobbled streets very early in the morning, making a terrible noise. The Montier-ini were awakened by the thundering and rum-bling. But since the room was pitch black because the wooden shutters were tightly closed, they thought it was still night and that a wild storm was raging.

Cried one Montierini: "Hear that unholy thun-der."

Said another: "It is a storm that will drown the world."

Spoke the third: "It's not so bad; we can sleep longer, which we can't do in Montieri."

"*Me si,*" all three said, and they closed their eyes and went to sleep.

Like most hard-working countryfolk, they were sound sleepers, and so they slept the whole day long, waking up when it was deep night. Then they thought they had had enough of sleeping.

Said one: "I will look out in the street and see what's going on." He opened the shutter and looked into the stony blackness.

"It's a long night, isn't it?" he said.

"Maybe the nights are longer in Siena than they are in Montieri," spoke another.

"Well, if it's night, it's night, and we should sleep," said the third.

"Me si," all three said, and back to sleep they went.

In the morning they got up, and one Montierini said, "I will open the window." He got up in the dark room and felt his way to what he believed was the shutter and opened it. It was dark and smelled of cheese.

"The street is still dark and smells of cheese," he cried. But, you see, he had opened the cupboard by mistake, and since the room was all in darkness, he did not see his error.

So back to sleep they went.

Meanwhile, the innkeeper was wondering what the three Montierini were doing closed up in the room for so many days. He went to their door and knocked loud enough to wake the dead.

64

"Wake up, you lazy fellows," he cried. "Wake up!"

"Me si, me si," the three cried, "we are awake."

"Haven't you had enough sleep?" the innkeeper asked.

"Me si, me si," they all shouted.

"Then why don't you get up and get out?" he cried.

"We are waiting for the sun to rise. This night has been as long as from Montieri to Jerusalem."

"You fools, the sun has risen the same as always the three days you have been sleeping in your room."

"And the *Palio?*" they cried.

"The *Palio* is finished and done, while you noodle-heads have been snoring. Did you think it would wait until you got up?"

"Me no, me no," they squeaked like little mice.

"Come, get up, you silly fools," the innkeeper said, "and pay me for the three days you have had the room or I'll drag you before the judge."

What could the Montierini do? They paid for the room and returned to Montieri not much wiser; for, as the saying goes, "fools don't learn by folly."

65

Nicola Pesce

The lovely land of Italy looks like a boot stretched out in the blue sea. And since the blue sea is full of fish of every color and size, there are many fishermen in Italy.

Now, there lived near Messina, in Sicily, right by Torre del Faro, young Nicola Pesce, the youngest of many sons of a fisherman. Nicola was different from all of his brothers. They loved to ride the sea, bringing in great catches of fish to be sold for hard money. But Nicola liked to roam the shore or stay at home playing with his pets and tending the little garden and looking at the gleaming shells from the green waters. He did not like to catch fish to kill.

Sometimes his father asked him to watch the basket full of fish that he and his other sons had caught, while they went off to attend to other affairs. When Nicola was alone with the fish he would look at them sadly and tell them how sorry he was for them. If any fish showed a little fluttering of life, he would throw it back into the sighing sea. One time his mother saw him doing this and gave him a hard, round scolding for it.

But the scoldings did not worry Nicola, nor did they stop his loving the sea and those who lived in it. He would spend whole days looking at the dancing waves, and soon he began diving into the vast blue water, playing with the finny folk. And then he would come home and tell of marvelous sights he had seen in the sea. His family and friends said it was crazy talk.

One day he returned with an extraordinary tale. "I was out swimming when there came rushing toward me a glistening whirlpool like a solid mass of silver-green whirling fish. It was racing on the water like a wild white horse. I got right in the middle of it and it carried me far, far away to Reggio Calabria. There, deep down, I saw miles of seaweed meadows with grazing life. I saw a great garden of rose and snow-white coral, beautiful as a king's palace. And all around were fish colored like golden mosaics in the church."

His mother thought her son had gone mad and went to the holy man in the mountains for help.

The man of God said, "Wash his shirt in holy water; sew a red ribbon around his belt; put an acorn in his pocket, and give him darnel bread to eat. That will make him well."

The mother did all this and prayed besides, but Nicola kept to the sea just the same and told tales of wondrous palaces deep in the wavy weedland. He spoke about sunken ships that looked like wild flowers, and of polyps dancing on the green, swaying, hairy grass.

So Nicola grew up in his sea-green world and became a famous diver known in every part of Italy.

One day Emperor Frederick II, King of Sicily, and his rosy daughter came to Messina, and they heard of Nicola Pesce. The Emperor summoned him to his palace.

"Everyone speaks of you as a marvelous diver. I want to see if it's true. Come out with me to my ship."

Out on the great ship they went—the Emperor, his daughter, the diver, and the crew. When they were far out, the Emperor threw a golden cup into the green sea.

"You bring it back," he said to Nicola.

Down dived the great diver, and soon he was back on the ship, the golden cup in one hand and in the other a coral branch more beautiful than any jewel.

The cup he gave to his liege and lord; the coral branch he gave to the beautiful princess.

"Keep the cup as a gift," the Emperor said, "and now get me my sword." He took his golden sword and threw it far out into the white churning waves.

Again Nicola dived in and brought up the sword.

"That any diver can do," said the Emperor. "Any diver can bring up a cup or a sword. Now I'll give you a task to really test your skill. I want to know on what the island of Sicily rests. I want to know its foundation all around. Dive down, swim all around the island, and come back and tell me."

Nicola looked at the proud Emperor and then at the rosy princess.

"I will," he said. "Wait for me." And down he went into the shimmering blue.

They waited and they waited. They waited for

days and days, until one day Nicola came up to the ship.

"Sire," said he, "Sicily rests on three granite columns stronger than mountains. But there is danger coming. One of the columns has a burning fire at the base that is slowly crumbling away the stone."

"In which direction stands this column?"

"Between Messina and Catania. The raging fire is making the water boil, and it is breaking the granite away bit by bit. No fish can come near, and all sea plants are gone."

"Did you go near it?" the Emperor asked.

"Only as far as where the red fire battles the black water for life or death."

"This is a strange tale," the Emperor said, "and I can hardly believe it. Bring me the fire from under the sea and then I will know that your words are true."

For a time Nicola was silent; then he spoke. "Sire, were I Saint Joseph I might bring it in the hem of my mantle, but I am only a common man," and he looked at the heaven-blue eyes of the Emperor's daughter.

"The story is that you are the greatest diver of all Messina," said the Emperor, "but I must have proof

to believe it. Bring the fire from the burning granite pillar and then I, too, will believe!"

The Emperor looked straight at him, and the
princess looked at the sea.

"Sire," said Nicola, "I will bring it to you." Down
he went in the green-white churning water. Deeper
and deeper he went. The water was black-blue;
deeper still, and the water was purple-dark. Suddenly it was bright, bright red, and he saw the wild
raging fire at the base of the column and the pounding water battling with it for life or death.

Struggling through the water, Nicola swam up
and tried to take the fire in his hands, but it slith-
ered through, burning his flesh, stabbing like cut-
ting knives.

Again and again he tried, but with no better luck.
So he rose up in the sea and came to the ship and
climbed up slowly. The pain in his hands nearly
numbed his tongue, and he spoke very slowly.

"Sire, I cannot bring the fire to you, but here are
my hands in which I tried to hold it. Look at them.
Do you believe me now?"

But power makes men hard. Said the Emperor:

"If you can't bring me the fire in your hands, I
want you to find out where it comes from, where it

goes, and how quickly it will crumble the whole column."

Nicola stood without saying a word. The light-blue eyes of the princess looked at the sea.

"You are not afraid, are you?" asked the Emperor.

"I am not afraid," said Nicola, "but if I go down this time, I will never return." And he looked again at the princess, but she never raised her eyes.

"Go," said the Emperor. "You will return in time and tell me."

"Everyone must die. Some go early, some late. But before I go, I want to see my father and mother and my home."

Nicola went to his home and spoke to his father and mother and brothers. He went to his little garden and watered his white jasmine bush and his red geraniums. Then, slowly, he went back to the ship, looked at the sky and at the land, then at the Emperor and at the rosy princess, and dived off.

The Emperor waited and waited, and so did the princess, and time went through weeks and months and years. The princess often thought of dark-eyed Nicola, who had given her a coral jewel more beautiful than any she had owned before, but he never came back.

Once, as she was walking along the sandy shore, she saw a whirlpool of water shaped like a great green mass of silvery fish, and from it came the voice of Nicola:

"Don't wait for me, beautiful princess. When I reached the fire under the granite pillar, it had crumbled away so much of the gray stone that the pillar began to sway, so I went under it to hold it up, and there I have stood ever since. I could not let Sicily fall. But the fire does not hurt me. Here I must stay until there is no pain or strife on the earth or in the sea. Then kindness will keep the pillar strong and steady."

And to this day folks say that Nicola Pesce, Nicola the Fish, is still deep in the sea, bracing one of the three pillars that holds up Sicily. And the fire is still raging, and the water is still battling, until kindness in the world shall end the strife.

Eat and Like It

Polenta is a thick corn-meal mush that peasants eat in all parts of Italy. It is served in many ways—with tomatoes, with different kinds of sauce, and sometimes even baked into hard bread and eaten with milk. Folks in Montieri, too, ate it in every way that it could be eaten.

They ate it in the morning, they ate it at noon, and they ate it at night. They had eaten polenta for a long, long time, and they were mighty tired of it. They grumbled and complained, and the young folks just wouldn't touch it and gave it to the dogs. But, sad to say, most of the time there was nothing else to eat; so the womenfolk went to the priest, Father Graziono, to talk to him about it.

"Father," they said, "the Lord is not kind to us. We are tired of polenta. All of us—men, women, and children—dislike it; even the dogs don't like it too much. We don't know what to do about it. Only you can help us. You must make us like it again or give us something else to eat."

Father Graziono answered, "I am much surprised at what you say. Polenta is a gift from God, and you should like the blessings of the Lord. But I think I can help you. Tomorrow we will start on a pilgrimage and we will not stop until you once again like polenta—the Lord's blessing."

The next morning all the folk of Montieri were at the square before the church. All wore pilgrim clothes: the men were in white cloaks, the women had veils on their heads and bore candles in their hands, and the boys and girls carried banners and torches.

Father Graziono came out sitting on his white mule.

"Let us start," he said, and off he went, with the Montierini following.

Slowly the mule began going up the mountain

with men, women, and children behind. They walked a long time, the dry hot sun covering them like a mantle, until they reached the first level, grassy ground.

Good Father Graziono stopped and cried, "Do you like polenta now?"

"*Me no, me no, me no,*" they cried all together.

The priest turned his mule's nose toward the mountain and again began climbing up. The sky was bright blue and the golden sun shone with fiery blessing. Sweat ran down the Montierini's foreheads, faces, and bodies, and there wasn't much talk.

They reached the second flat piece of ground. The priest stopped, thinking of the good proverb: "When hunger gets strong, pride becomes weak." So he asked, "Do you like polenta now?"

"*Me no, me no,*" they all shouted from dry throats, licking their lips with their tongues.

On and on went the priest up the mountain, with the others behind, until they came to a flat piece of ground, and again Father Graziono stopped and cried:

"Do you like polenta now?"

It was noon, and the fiery sun stood right in the middle of the blue heaven, shining daggers on the

Montierini. They were hot and tired enough to drop, but still they did not like polenta, and when the priest asked the old question again they all shouted:

"*Me no, me no.*"

Higher and higher mule and master went up the mountain, the folk of Montieri dragging behind. The sun was going down the heaven very, very slowly, and all were hungry as wolves in the winter and too tired to breathe. They were nearing the top of the mountain and they were breathing heavily. Father Graziono stopped for a minute and cried:

"Do you like polenta now?"

From empty stomachs and weary feet came a low cry: "*Me si, me si,*" which means "yes."

Quickly the priest turned the mule's head down the mountain. The beast knew the way to the stable and now went rapidly. So did the folks of Montieri, stumbling pell-mell over brush and stone, and soon they were back in their own beloved home town. What a great surprise greeted them! In the center of the square was a big table covered with steaming hot, delicious polenta and fine drink. The wise priest, knowing people's ways, had ordered his own household to prepare the good food, knowing full well that hunger is the finest blessing for a good appetite. All the Montierini sat down joyfully and had the best meal they had ever had in all their lives. When they were through, they thanked their wise priest and the good Lord for making them want and for giving them their good polenta once again.

A Flower for a Husband!

In the days of bold knights, there was a beautiful girl whom many courted but who could not find any man to suit her. This girl had an aunt who loved her very dearly. The aunt, a good and wise woman who knew the art of sorcery, was often visited by the girl. One day the aunt said to her:

"All your friends are married, and though nearly all the young fellows in the village court you, you run from them like a mouse from a cat."

"Honestly, auntie," the girl said, "I want to be married but there is not one I love. All the men of the village are country bumpkins."

"You are too choosy, niece, and you are passing

by many a fine stone because it seems rough on the outside."

"I will only marry a gentleman."

"When the right one comes along, you will forget whether he is high- or low-born and you will run after him," the wise woman said laughingly.

But weeks passed and months passed and our pretty girl was still without a sweetheart, though all her friends were happily wedded.

One day the girl was visiting her aunt and they were discussing the same subject. Lovely Maria was sad, and her aunt was becoming so impatient that she decided to take a hand in the business.

"Maria," said she, "one of these days you'll wake up and find yourself an old maid. It is time I do something about this. Now, you do as I tell you. Do you see that stone house at the corner? You go in there and you will see three high-born gentlemen. They are handsome and rich, and they are sitting at a table singing and drinking. Any one of the three will be happy to marry you. It is up to you to choose the one you want."

The girl went to the stone house, entered a room, and there she found the three gentlemen exactly as her aunt had said she would.

At first she could not make up her mind which of the three she liked best, but in the end she chose the one with the dark hair and the dark eyes. The two were wed and went happily to their upstairs chamber in the stone house. Before Maria looked thrice around the room she was sound asleep, and when the rich sun shone through the window and she awoke—she was all alone! No sight or sound of the handsome gentleman. But on top of the coverlet was a beautiful dark-flaming flower, sweet-scented like roses on a June night. She cried and called out, but all her crying and calling was of little use. The only answer was the cinnamon-warm scent of the flower on the embroidered coverlet.

So the girl went weeping to her aunt and said, "Good aunt, sweet aunt, the fine gentleman I wedded is gone, and there is only a dark-red cinnamon-scented flower on my coverlet. I don't want sweet-scented flowers; I want a husband!"

The aunt smiled and said, "Go back to the room in the stone house and choose another of the noble gentlemen. You left two there singing and drinking."

So the girl went back to the house, and there were the two gentlemen still singing and drinking.

Again she could not make up her mind which one she wanted. In the end, she chose the one with the emerald-green eyes clad in the lemon and black checkered doublet. The two were wed and went into the chamber on the upper floor. Again the girl fell asleep at the wink of an eye, and when she awoke the next morning—she was all alone again. No sign or sound of her lord. But on the embroidered coverlet lay a beautiful long lemon-yellow flower from which came a full, delicate, sweet perfume— the kind you smell after the sun has set. Maria cried and called, but the only echo was the sweet perfume of the flower on the embroidered coverlet. The maid did not want the perfume; she wanted her liege and lord, so she put the lemon-yellow flower next to the dark-red flower in a vase of colored Venetian glass and ran to her aunt.

The wise lady listened to her crying and sighs and said, "Niece, go back to the stone house and see if you love the third gentleman well enough to marry him."

So she returned for the third time and said she would marry the last gentleman because he was high-born and rich. The two were wedded and went to their chamber above, and once again she fell

asleep the moment she looked at the ceiling. When she awoke—she was all alone for the third time, and on the white coverlet of her bed was a pure white flower, holy as a hymn. The room was filled with a perfume sweeter than the taste of honey, but the poor girl did not even know it, she was so angry. She picked up the lovely white flower and pushed it into the vase with the other two and ran with the vase to her aunt.

"Here are the men I married," she cried, "thanks to your magic, and what have I to show? Three flowers! I don't want any flowers, I want a husband. Here, take them!" and she put the vase on the table with a bang.

"Now, good niece," said the wise woman, "don't spurn these lovely flowers. They are beautiful indeed, and sweeter-scented than any I ever smelled. I'll join them together in such a way that they will make a single flower of special beauty—so wondrous that it will go into the shield of Florence to adorn it and make it known forever to all the world.

"As for your worries, my dear niece, perhaps this will teach you to marry one of your own kind and not a nobleman. Pick some nice young man in the village who will bring you a simple, happy life—the kind your friends have."

And so it happened that the lovely girl married a fine countryman. And the old aunt fashioned a marvelously beautiful *giglio,* the lily that you see sculptured even today in the shield of Florence.

A Miracle of a Saint

Years ago there lived in the mountains near Salerno in Italy a little girl. She never saw any neighbors; she never spoke to anyone. She saw only the Lord with her eyes, and day and night she spoke to Him with prayers.

She was virtuous and kind to all insects and animals and beasts—she really lived the life of a saint.

One day she decided to go to the city. She walked down the mountains into the valley until she reached the shore by the sea. There were many boats with gaily colored sails, and fishermen sat on the yellow sand mending their nets.

"Where will I find a holy church in which to pray?" she said to the fishermen.

The men, busy mending the brown nets, looked up at her and answered jokingly with a little song.

> *"Cuofine salie e cuofine shene,*
> *Santa sportele aiuteme tu."*

This means among the Neapolitan fishermen:

> *"Basket go up and basket go down,*
> *Saint porthole* [a place in which they
> put their fish] *help me!"*

Again she said, "Where will I find a church? I want to pray in it."

And again they answered:

> *"Cuofine salie e cuofine shene,*
> *Santa sportele aiuteme tu."*

She asked the fishermen the same question for the third time, and again they repeated the same words, and then they said, "You just say these words and you are sure to find a church."

So she walked along the shore repeating all the time:

> *"Cuofine salie e cuofine shene,*
> *Santa sportele aiuteme tu."*

Soon she saw three mauve sea gulls floating slowly down the green water; then they flew up into the big sky and went off into the far-away blue, where a boat with sails stood silently. It was all so lovely to see that she stopped saying the words. And then, when she tried to say them again, she could not— she had forgotten them. She ran back to where the fishermen had been, but when she got there they were not to be seen. They had gone in their green boats out onto the blue water. She shouted and she shouted, asking for the words to find the church, but all her shouting was in vain. The fisherman were too far from shore to hear her.

She had to know the words, for she had to find the church. And she became so excited and so eager that she forgot everything and began running in—no, *on* the water toward the boats of the fishermen. She ran on that ripply blue water as if it were solid dry land.

The fishermen stopped fishing and sat or stood in their boats, filled with astonishment, looking at the miracle before their eyes. They knew they were beholding a great holy wonder that could be performed only by a saint. And from that time on the girl has been regarded as a saint by the people living around Salerno.

The Sun Will
Always Shine

In rich golden-domed Venice by the sea there dwelt a rich gentleman whose head was turned by money and power. He thought he could do anything in the world—even change the ways and nature of man and animal.

"I shall begin with animals," he said in his silly conceit.

So he began with cats and dogs and horses. He had a great deal of patience, and in good time he taught his horse to eat meat and his dog to eat hay. He took a donkey and taught him how to dance, and he taught two fish to run a race. And he also taught his cat to hold a lighted candle in her paw while eating her meal.

He was prouder of that cat and of what she did than of any of the other animals. While some of the others sometimes failed in their new tasks, the cat always obeyed her master's orders. Nothing would disturb her while holding that candle and eating. Whenever the man had a chance, he would have the animals display their new accomplishments before his friends.

"You see, good fellows," he would say, "this proves to you that the nature of animals can be changed completely, and so can the nature of man."

Of course, his friends did not agree with him. They told him that although you may change the habits of beasts, their nature remains the same. Nature has its own laws. You can't change the moon or the stars, and the sun will always shine.

"I proved to you what I believe—that I can change nature; but you have not proved to me what you believe—that it cannot be changed. I dare one of you to turn any of my animals from their new habits—particularly my cat."

Now, among those who were listening there was one, Silvio by name, who was as smart and clever as a fox. He thought about the matter a great deal and finally hit upon a scheme.

Silvio went out and caught a tiny mouse. The next time he visited his "wizard" friend he waited for the cat trick. The mouse was in his pocket. Now, you must know the "wizard" was by then so proud and so blown up by his own importance that he displayed his animals with their new tricks every time anyone came to visit him.

One after another, all the animals did their unusual acts. Then came the white cat. She sat there holding a candle with her paw while lapping milk from a saucer.

And just then Silvio took the mouse out of his pocket and put it on the table. The mouse scuttled along. No sooner did the cat see it than she dropped the candle, forgot the milk, and began chasing the mouse.

A great laugh went up from all the company.

"You see, my good friend," cried Silvio, "all the teaching in the world will not change that which nature has implanted in us. It may change some little things, but that with which we are born, that which God gave us, is always with us. Remember, friend, the sun will always shine."

Wise Words with Golden Profit

In the olden days many of the greatest artists and craftsmen who ever lived came from Italy, the warm land where golden-yellow lemons bloom. For that reason you will hear many tales about these creators of beauty—about how they lived and how they did their wonderful work. Some of these stories came from the bright land of laughter and some from the gray realm of sadness, and some from the gray-bright land where both are found.

You must know that in those days the great artists were helped by rich, noble families, and, in return for the aid given them, the men of genius beautified their patrons' great palaces with paintings, sculpture, and other arts. Each family tried to secure the finest artists and paid them well for their labor.

Now, there lived in Florence in those early days two noble families, the Strozzi and the Pitti families, and each built a magnificent palace, as was the custom of the time. When the Strozzis had finished theirs, the Pittis built a larger one to show what *they* could do. To beat this, the Strozzis decided to beautify theirs with marvelous ornaments that the Pitti palace did not have. They ordered many adornments for their stone buildings, and among them, from Niccolò Grosso, the great metal craftsman, four lanterns so delicately wrought and turned, so fancifully and beautifully designed, that their equal could not be found anywhere in Italy.

Niccolò set to work. He studied countless plans and endless curling designs and rounded figures. Then he began to look for proper metal for the work. He would do justice to his name as a craftsman, and he would do honor to the family that wanted only great art in their home.

But alas! The wondrous roses of art are covered with sharp-aching thorns, and rich folk often forget that the poor are not rich. The Strozzi nobles soon forgot to give Niccolò money for his living costs and materials.

Now, Niccolò Grosso loved good living as well as good jesting. He was known for his bluntness and independence, even as he was known for his craftsmanship, and he would not work for any man, even a noble, if he were not paid properly. The forgetfulness of the Strozzis filled him with anger, for there was other work he could have taken on.

One morning he was seated on a bench before his shop eating a dry piece of bread. He was not in a pleasant humor, and his face showed this clearly.

Along came a countryman carrying a basket of young, fat purple-red onions, rosy-red radishes, and green peppers. The man stopped before Niccolò.

"You look angry, good friend," said he, "and I don't wonder. Any man would be, eating dry bread for breakfast."

"That's what a man has to eat when he works for rich nobles," grumbled Niccolò. "They think an artist must be pleased with poor pottage, but this time they have the wrong artist!"

"You are an artist?"

"That I am, indeed. My name is Niccolò Grosso, and the great Strozzi family has asked me to make some fine wrought lanterns for their palace."

"Then you should not be in want. The Strozzis are rich and surely can well afford to give you money to buy onions and radishes for your bread."

"Ha, so they are, friend, only they believe in the old proverb that poor folk must be pleased with little favors. They have not given me money for food or for materials."

"Well, Signore Grosso, I am not a rich Strozzi, but here, take some good juicy onions and fine firm radishes to flavor your bread."

Niccolò thanked the old man, took some, and invited him to sit on the bench, which he did.

"Good fellow Niccolò," the old man said, "I have heard about you and that you are a blunt man who loves a good jest, so here is what I would advise you to do. I am older than you are, and I have seen many years of life and have known many men. Now, you take my basket of onions and stand in front of the Strozzi palace gate. When your rich patrons come out, offer to sell them onions. Then, when they ask you why you are selling onions instead of working on the lanterns, tell them you have to do this to earn money for food and materials for their work. If that does not shame them into giving you the money you need, I will lend you the gold to finish your work of art."

"Why do you offer to lend me money? You hardly know me—I am really a stranger to you."

"You are no stranger. A fine craftsman is a friend of every man. I am old and I have learned to know that money is of little value save for the comfort and pleasure it brings—and your work brings me even greater pleasure."

Niccolò, who, as I told you, loved a good jest, did exactly as the old man had advised him.

When the noble Strozzis came strutting from their towering palace gate they saw a crowd and heard the shouting:

"Rich juicy onions for sale! Here are firm red radishes like pretty birds! You can buy them cheap."

The nobles stopped, their eyes wide open when they saw it was their artist, Niccolò Grosso, selling onions like a common country clout.

"And why aren't you at work on our lanterns?" a lady cried in a high-pitched voice.

Then Niccolò told his story, just as the old man had advised him: that he had to sell onions and rad-

ishes to earn money for food and to pay for the materials for the lanterns. The nobles were so ashamed
that they gave him, then and there, a large sum of
money and told him proudly to make the lanterns of
gold!

Niccolò was overjoyed, and when he met the old
gentleman again he thanked him over and over for
his good advice, telling him that it had not only
helped him get his money but that he now had been
ordered to make the lanterns of gold, which was
used only for jewels. Niccolò added:

"Your wise words helped me to golden profit,
even as the light from the lanterns will help the
Florentines not to fall into ruts and ditches."

"Since you were wise and took my advice, I will
give you some more for your benefit," said the old
fellow. "First, keep some of these onions and study
them well. Their shape and leaves are finely shaped
and may help you in carving your designs for the
lanterns. Second, remember that iron comes from
Mother Earth just as gold does, and is much stronger.
If you make your lanterns of gold, they will tempt
thieves to steal them and melt them. That will never
happen to iron—iron will last for all time to come."

Niccolò Grosso was wise, though young in years.

He knew he could learn from those older than himself. So he studied the shape and the graceful folding of the yellow-white leaves of the onions and made his lanterns in a long and delicate design not unlike onion sprouts. He made them of iron, in ornaments and figures, in curvings and filigrees and flourishes like the finest jewelry. Truly, they were a marvel of beauty. In the end he gilded them. So they seemed of gold, but instead they were made of strong, honest iron.

Niccolò loved the old man who had given him this good advice and he went traveling with him throughout the land. As for the massive Strozzi stone palace, it still stands in Florence today, and you can still see the marvelously wrought iron lanterns shaped like onion sprouts. They are as beautiful today as when Niccolò Grosso made them in the heyday of his years.

The Lost Paradise

Once there lived an old husband and his wife, who were hard-working and honest but who always wished life could be a little easier. After the day's work they would talk of their hard lives.

"Wife, do you know that if Eve had not been so curious, we would now be in the Garden of Eden without work and worry and with plenty to eat?"

"She just wanted the wrong apple," the wife answered.

"There were plenty of other things to eat in that garden, I wager, and plenty of trees. Why did she have to eat apples from just that one tree? I would never have touched it. Never!"

Now, it so happened that just then their master was under their window and heard their talk. He smiled and said to himself:

"I wonder if they could keep from looking at and touching what was forbidden to them. Why not try them? I would like to see."

He went into their house and said, "Good people, why not come to my *palazzo,* and I will give you fine rooms in which to live and I will feed you fine food. You will have everything in the world you want, just as if you were in Paradise."

"Oh, that would be a blessing from Heaven," they both cried.

"You can stay there as long as you wish. Oh, yes, I forgot—there is one little thing. On your table there will be one dish you may not open. It is a brown covered terrina."

"Oh, that is easy," the man cried.

"Remember," the nobleman said, "don't uncover that dish or you will lose your Paradise, just as Adam and Eve lost theirs."

"We won't, we won't," the woman said. "Why

103

touch that one dish when there will be so many others on the table?"

"Don't forget, you must not open the brown covered terrina on the table."

"We will never open it," both the man and his wife said fervently.

They came to the palace and were housed in a beautiful chamber and had a servant to wait on them. The nobleman asked the servant to tell him when they opened the covered terrina standing in the middle of the table.

The two old people really were in Paradise. They had everything they wanted: a fine large room and three meals a day fit for a noble. They sat at a grand table lit with candles and had a servant in attendance. On the table stood dishes with tasty, steaming food, and they could sample each dish as much as their hearts desired.

In the center of the table stood the covered terrina. At first they hardly noticed it. The husband just said, "That is the dish we must not touch."

Every time they sat down the husband merely glanced at it, and so did the wife.

"We should not look at it," she said the second day, "and I wish it were not there."

"Well, we can look at it without opening it, wife. And who wants to open it when there are so many other fine dishes to open?"

But with each meal they talked about it more. Besides, since they had become used to the fine food, eating it every day, they demanded more and more from the servant. They even spoke differently.

"I can't understand why we can't open that terrina," said the wife. The sickness of curiosity had gotten into her and gave her no peace. As you know, a curious woman is like a stormy sea. She never stopped talking to her husband about that terrina. Finally she said:

"Suppose we just open it a little bit at the edge."

"Wife, remember what the Count said."

"Why did he say it? What's in it that is so precious that we can't see? We won't take it away from him." She was rapidly getting angrier.

"Just let us lift it a little bit on the edge. It will do no harm to anyone, and no one will ever find out."

"Maybe he won't, but I am afraid, wife."

She kept on talking, and in the end—for he was curious, too, though he would not admit it—he said:

"Well, lift it up just a little on one side, and we'll take a little peep."

That was enough for the wife. She stood up and reached out for the terrina, opened it a tiny crack on one side, and—out flew a little bird! The two sat speechless!

The servant went at once to his lord and told him what had happened, and out from the *palazzo* the two had to go. Curiosity had lost them their Paradise, even as it had lost Paradise to Adam and Eve.

A Lesson Well Learned

Not far from Padua, from which many learned men have come, lived a blacksmith who was an honest man and a fine craftsman, but he had one weakness: he was swollen with blind pride. He carried his head high as the sky, even with his nearest kin. If a man just came to have his horse shod, he would do it only if the man called him "professor." When he walked in the street he wanted folks to talk to him as though he were a prince. You can just imagine what most people thought of him. They said he was a fine man but that pride was making him a silly one.

Now, one day the good Lord and Saint Peter were walking along the sunny road and came to that blacksmith's smithy. The Blessed Lord took one look at him and saw at once what sort of person the blacksmith was.

"Good Signore and Professor," the Lord said, "would you permit me to use your fire and forge? I have a little piece of work I would like to do."

The blacksmith was much flattered by these honeyed words and answered:

"Messire, fire and forge are at your command. Pray, do your work here. But what work do you want to do?"

"Nothing very important, and I am sure you could do it better. But once I helped a blacksmith and I would like to try my hand at it."

"Just go ahead and work."

Then the Lord took up the largest tongs he could find and picked up Saint Peter with them. It was truly a funny sight to see old, bald-headed Saint Peter dangling in the air. The Lord put the good saint right into the leaping fire. Saint Peter never said a word, for he trusted completely in the Lord; besides, he felt no pain and knew what was coming.

The Lord held the saint in the fire until he was

red hot and then he took him out and put him on the anvil, picked up a big hammer, and began hammering him this way and that way and every way. Pretty soon the good old bald-headed saint was young and fresh as a twenty-year-old, and on his bald head he had fine black hair falling down his back. The blacksmith, seeing this, was so surprised you could have thrown him down with a straw.

Then the Lord and young Saint Peter thanked the speechless blacksmith for his hospitality and went their way.

The blacksmith stood for a time, thinking. Then he raised his head up high, and pride ran through every bone in his body.

"If that blacksmith can do it, I can do it, too," he said. He ran into the room in which his very old father lay ill and weak.

"Father," he cried, "I have just learned a wonderful new art of making old people young. Now I'll truly be a professor. Come, you'll be the first on whom I'll practice."

The old man argued and told his son how silly he was, but it did no good at all. He was dragged into the smithy, though he cried and protested. Before he knew what was happening, the son shouted:

"Father, I do this because I love you. I will make a new young man of you," and he put the old man right into the red fire. There he kept him until there remained only a golden glow and a few charred bones.

He took out the bones and began pounding them just as he had seen the Lord do. But alas! all he got was gray dust. He became terribly frightened, for he loved his father dearly and had done the awful deed because he wanted to make him well and young. He cried and shouted and ran out looking for the strangers. Up and down the narrow streets he ran, tearing his hair and crying wildly. Suddenly, in the market place, he saw the two strangers wandering around looking at the lovely colored fruit and fish and fowl.

He rushed up to them, crying: "Kind sir, kind sir!" and he grabbed hold of the Lord's arm. "A terrible thing has happened. I tried to do with my old father what you did with this young man," and he pointed to the saint, "and he is all burned. Oh, sir, you must help me mend this terrible wrong. You must. I have done a terrible thing. I don't want to live!"

Spoke the Lord: "Since you feel as you do, and I

know you speak the truth, I will help you. Go home. There you will find your father alive and well —but not a young man. And remember not to be overproud, for pride is the beginning of sin."

The distracted blacksmith ran home, just shouting his thanks and greetings, and when he came into the smithy there was his father, hale and hearty. He cried for joy, and then he told him the whole story, adding, "This is to teach me that I am not the great man I think I am."

"Yes, my son," the father said, "you were riding a mighty high horse, forgetting you are not a knight."

From then on, if anyone called the blacksmith "sir" or "professor," he would say quickly:

"There are professors in Padua and there are sirs in Venice. I am just a blacksmith in my village, and happy to be one."

The Wisdom of Cecchino

It is told that long ago—though it could have happened yesterday—there lived in Apulia, the region of olives and grapes at the "heel" of Italy, a woman who had three sons. One of the three just didn't like to work. His name was Cecchino, which means "little Francesco." He believed a fellow could live by his wits just as well as by his muscles. His brothers said he was lazy, and they were forever telling their mother to send the lazy lout away. But a mother loves all sons alike, so she said:

"He isn't so bad as you make him. Why not give him a wife? When he has a wife, he will work."

A wife he got, but do you think that made him work? No, he still believed a busy head was as good as busy hands. Now his two brothers had to work not only for him but for his wife as well. They did not like that one bit, so they kept at their mother to send him away, until finally she just had to do it. Besides, she thought it would do the boy good. With a sorrowful face she told him the bad news.

"Mother, you don't have to look so sad," said Cecchino, smiling. "Don't worry. God will help me, and my head isn't green cabbage, either. One day I'll come back a rich man."

He took his pretty young wife by the arm, and they both went off gaily into the wide world. Soon Cecchino felt hungry.

"I could eat something, pretty one," he said.

"So could I," said she.

"You know, lovely dark-eyes," said Cecchino, "I've been doing a little thinking. Now, I don't like hard work and I've figured out some work that is not hard and will give us what we want: it is fishing. All you need do is sit with a string in your hand. I am going fishing and I'll catch enough to feed us and to sell so we can have a little money."

They went to the blue sea, sat down on the warm

yellow sand, and Cecchino cast a line into the dancing water. Soon he felt a hard tugging. He pulled and he pulled and his wife had to help him. In the end the two pulled up a fish bigger than a man.

"That is a fish of fishes," Cecchino cried, "and it'll make our fortune. Come, pretty one, we will take it to the King and he'll pay us well."

So they went to the city of the King's palace.

Now, you know a king always has many servants around him, and many of them are the kind who will take the skin off your back for a favor.

When Cecchino came to the gatekeeper of the palace and told him he wanted to see the King, and why, the gatekeeper said:

"If you give me half of your reward for that fish, I'll let you in."

"That I'll do with pleasure," Cecchino said.

In he went and up the marble stairs. At the head stood the third valet of the King.

"Where to?" he asked, and Cecchino told him.

"I'll let you go to the King if you give me half of your reward for that fine fish."

Cecchino smiled and promised quickly.

At the door he met the second valet of the King, and he also asked for half, and Cecchino made him

the same promise. When he saw the first valet, he, too, wanted half the reward, and Cecchino promised him just as he had promised all the others.

Then he saw the King, who was pleased indeed at the sight of that wonderful fish.

"So you brought it to me as a present," he said.

"Yes, Your Majesty, I thought such a fine fish would fit the royal table."

"Thank you, young fellow," the King said, "and as a reward I will give you one hundred golden lire."

"Thanks, Your Majesty, you are very kind, but do you mind if I ask for one hundred good lashes with a whip instead? I can use them well as a good lesson."

"Well, I never heard of a fellow who wanted flogging on his back instead of money in his pocket, but, then, there are different kinds of folk in this world."

"Thanks, Your Majesty. Now call the gatekeeper."

"What for?" asked the King.

"He would not let me see you unless I would give him half of my reward for the fish."

"Ah," said the King, smiling, "I see the way the wind blows."

So the greedy gatekeeper was called and got his share of the reward.

"Now you get the rest," the King said.

"No, I don't, Your Majesty. Your third valet would not let me see you unless I promised him half of my reward."

"Oho," cried the King, and the valet was called and was given half of the remainder of the lashes as a reward for his greediness.

"Who's next?" the King asked.

"Your second valet, Your Majesty."

So he was called, and received half of the remainder of the lashes for his dishonesty.

"Who comes now, my smart young man?" cried the King.

"Your first valet. He, too, wanted a share."

"Oh, he too! What a fine lot of servants I have! Get him and let him have his full share."

So he got his share, which was half the remainder.

"Now, there are six strokes left that belong to you, Cecchino."

"Wait, Your Majesty. You know that people are greedy in this world. Some, hearing I have gotten six strokes from the King, won't believe it. They may think it is gold. Let us see if I am right."

The King laughed and agreed, so Cecchino went out into the market place of the city and began crying:

"Who'll buy six good strokes as a gift from the King? Who'll buy six good, fine lashes from our good, generous King?"

Believe it or not, it didn't take long until a man came along who offered to buy them for a good sum. He thought the strokes from the King meant something of great value.

Cecchino led him to the courtyard of the palace and there he got the six lashes, which made him a wiser man.

"Young fellow," the King said, "you have more wisdom than your years, and I think both will grow with time. Stay with me and be my gatekeeper, for you will know whom to let in and how to let them in."

So Cecchino became the royal gatekeeper, which was the kind of work he wanted. He sat the long day in the golden sun and used his wits instead of his muscles.

Why Donkeys Have Long Ears

When the holy Lord created the green world, He made all animals, just as you read in the Bible. And, as you know, among these was a gray-black, four-footed donkey that was no different from any other animal.

The good Lord gave each creature its name, but the donkey was so busy munching juicy thistles that he did not listen. So, as the animals went into the world, the donkey asked:

"Good Lord, what is my name?"

"Donkey," the Lord said, and the donkey went his way, pleased as a peacock.

He ate thistles and young green leaves the long sunny day. Sometimes he rolled on the grass and opened his mouth wide, he was so happy. Soon he forgot his name. So he went to the Lord and said:

"Good Lord, I forgot my name. Please tell it to me again."

The Lord looked kindly at the little animal and said:

"Your name is Donkey."

So Donkey went off, braying with pleasure.

The growing days went by. The young butterflies played in the fat grass and the donkey was busy from morning to night, eating and rolling on the ground—and once again he forgot his name. So he ran to the Lord and for a third time asked Him to please tell him his name.

Patiently the Lord told him his name was Donkey.

Time went by, and for the fourth time Donkey forgot his name. He came to the Lord for the fourth time.

"Excuse me, good Lord," he said, and his head was bowed low, "excuse me, Lord, but I have forgotten my name again."

Now, this was the fourth time the donkey had

asked for his name, and you cannot blame the Lord for losing patience a little. He got hold of Donkey by the ears and, pulling them, though not too hard, he said slowly:

"For the fourth time I am telling you that your name is Donkey. Donkey! Donkey! Don't forget it. Donkey!"

And do you know, this time Donkey did not forget his name. Though the Lord had pulled the ears gently, still they had stretched and now they were very long. And every time Donkey saw his ears, reflected in a pond or a stream, he remembered his name. Since that time donkeys have had long ears so that they should not forget their name.

Red Flowers
in White Snow

More years ago than you can count, there lived at the foot of the Alps a little girl by the name of Anna Maria, who knew nothing about happiness. She was a hunchback, and her parents looked on her with harsh eyes. She was never given any pretty clothes and she was always scolded.

"I am ashamed to go out with your daughter," (that is what he always called Anna Maria) the father would say to the mother.

"If she were only a boy and could help on the land," the mother said.

"Here I am, working like a slave, and my only

son, Tommaso, is out in the world, we don't know where, while your daughter only disgraces us."

Poor Anna Maria! She cried in silence and was forever praying to God for Tommaso to return, for they were all badly in need of him. They were very poor, so poor that they had not paid the rent for their home and had been told that if it were not paid by Christmas they would have to get out. Besides that, the father coughed so hard it tore his chest apart, and there wasn't any money for the doctor or for medicine.

Christmas had come, and it was a sad Christmas in that household. Poor little Anna Maria offered to get some pine twigs to hang around the walls and gather a little wood for kindling, but all she got were dark looks and grumbling from her parents. The poor little girl walked out of the house to cry.

There was a great white silence that Christmas night out under the stars. It was silver clear and looked like a vast cathedral with a dark-blue dome filled with millions of dancing stars.

"If I were a boy and if I were not a hunchback, my parents would be nice to me," she thought, and she cried. It was so cold the tears nearly froze on her cheeks, but she was so unhappy she did not feel them.

Suddenly she saw coming toward her a tall angel with wings shining like silver. The angel came up and said:

"Little girl, stop your crying. Think quickly of three wishes, three things you would like in life."

Anna Maria thought she was dreaming. "What three wishes?" she asked.

"Three Christmas wishes. Anyone who meets me after I bring the little Christ Child to the earth for the holiday worship can ask me for three things. But please hurry. It is a very cold night and neither of us should be out."

Anna Maria was terribly excited. Of course, her first thought was to get rid of the hump on her back, but then, she thought, that could wait. Something more important should come first.

"I want my brother, Tommaso, to come back, for my parents have been very unhappy since he has been away," she said quickly, her teeth chattering with cold.

"Granted," the angel said at once.

"And next I want much, much money for my father and mother so they can pay the rent and not have to get out of the house."

"Granted," the angel said again.

How easy it was to get what you wanted! she thought.

"And then," she cried, "I want my father to be well. He coughs all the time and says he has a pain in his chest." And then, she thought to herself, I want that hump to go off my back so that I can be a straight little girl like all the other little girls——But before she could talk of herself, the angel was gone. She remembered that she had made three wishes and the wish about herself was the fourth wish.

She turned slowly homeward.

"Well, it was all a dream, anyway. I know very well people don't get what they want just by saying it."

When she arrived at their small house she heard shouting voices. Picture her surprise when she looked in through the window and saw her brother, Tommaso, laughing with her father and mother. She saw much gold on the table. And her father did not seem to be ill any more.

"So it wasn't a dream!" she cried, rushing into the house.

"What was not a dream?" her father said, hardly looking at her.

"It is only Anna Maria, talking nonsense as she always does," said the mother. "Child, you had better go to bed."

Even her brother hardly greeted her. She went sadly into her little room under the roof where she slept, crying to herself.

She walked to the window that had no panes. The cloth that was stuffed in to keep the cold out had fallen down. There she stood, looking into the cold silvery world, and the tears came faster and faster, falling into the white snow. When they touched the snow they turned blood-red, for they were tears of sorrow that came from her heart.

Suddenly the angel stood before her once again.

"Little Anna Maria," the angel said, "you had three wishes and you wished to make others happy, forgetting about yourself. For that you will be granted the wish you thought of last. A wish all for yourself." Anna Maria had stopped crying; she put her hand slowly to her back . . . it was all straight. She began crying for joy.

That is the story folks tell at the foot of the Alps in the northern part of Italy. And to prove it they show you little green branches with red berries, the holly you find at Christmastime in those parts. They say these are the tears of Anna Maria, who loved others so much she forgot about herself.

The Story
of the Stone Hen

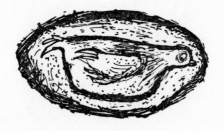

This is the tale of an old, old woman named Furricchia, who lived in an old, old stone house, in an old market place, in an ancient city of great beauty.

Over the door of the old stone house was a carved stone hen. She was a magic hen who helped Furricchia earn a fine living in a magic way. People in the neighborhood could not understand this and said it was very odd, though there wasn't really anything very odd about it. Everyone asked: where did Furricchia get her eggs? She never bought them from the countrymen who came early in the morning to the city to sell their wares. She never bought them from the merchants in the city. Yet the more eggs she sold, the more eggs she had to sell. Where did she get them?

Jealous tongues cackled and many of the villagers looked on Furricchia with evil envy. More jealous than all the others was one old lady who once had been rich but had lost her wealth and who now sold eggs, too. What she thought and said about the old egg-woman would make green frogs blush red. She was sure the Devil had a hand in it. If she could only prove that! Then she would have Furricchia burned as a witch. She and all the other poison-tongued gossips watched Furricchia day and night in the hope they would see a tailed Devil around the old stone house. But of course they never did, for the old lady was a God-loving soul and shunned the Devil as much as she loved the saints.

The old egg-woman was forever doing good to those who were in need. More than that, the eggs she sold had great healing power and cured many an illness. If those jealous people had only known the secret! It was all so simple. The stone hen over the door was hundreds of years old—from the days of the ancient Romans. In the olden days this hen's life had been saved by a kind girl, and in gratitude for the good deed the hen had fed the girl when she needed food most and none would give it to her. That happened when she became a Christian and all her pagan relatives tried to starve her into denying her belief in the Lord. Then the hen had laid eggs without end, and it was on these that the devout girl had lived. For that the good Lord had given the hen grace to continue living in stone and laying eggs for anyone who was truly kind and charitable and led a life such as the Lord desires people to lead. Now the hen was laying eggs for Furricchia because she lived like a true Christian.

Furricchia knew all this, and, being a simple woman, she saw nothing wonderful in herself or in her miraculous hen. She was just a faithful believer, and the Lord helped her in His own divine way.

Very early every morning, just as the great sun came up in the sky, the hen from over the door came down and laid a basketful of eggs and then flew back to the place where she always sat. Furricchia then sold the basketful of eggs in the market.

One morning, before the hen returned to her place, she said to her mistress, "Good Furricchia, your enemy, the once-rich lady, is getting sick with anger and envy because you have such good eggs to sell. These two poisons, anger and envy, have filled her so full that she is almost bursting with fury. She plans to come to your house today to try to learn how you get the eggs and bring you to court on some evil charge."

"Good hen, what can I do?" asked Furricchia.

"You cannot do anything. Remember, envy never dies, but it destroys itself in the end. But I will help you. I have thought of a little scheme that will teach the evil woman a lesson she will never forget. I still remember some magic from the pagan days.

"Before you go to the market, Furricchia, brew a pitcher of wine and put in the herbs I will name. Leave it steaming on the fire and go your way. When that green-eyed monster comes, I will do the rest."

Then she flew up over the door to listen to the endless talk of those who passed by. Furricchia made the brew and then went to the market to sell her eggs.

Soon the jealous-blind woman came. She called Furricchia's name twice, and when she got no answer, she began to look in corners and on shelves in the hope of finding something wrong.

Suddenly there was a hen-clucking sound and a voice coming from right over the door. To her great

surprise she heard the stone hen talking. "I need a little of the wine brewing on the hearth to help me lay more eggs. Whoever drinks that magic drink will lay eggs forever and a day."

At once the old woman rushed to the hearth, picked up the pot, hot as it was, and drank the brew down to the last drop. Then, having done something she had no right to do, she was smitten with fear and quickly sneaked out of the house and through the streets to her own home.

No sooner did she get into her house than she began clucking like a hen and feeling a queer pain in her legs and soon . . . soon . . . she began laying eggs. She was surprised, but happy because now she would have as many, and more, eggs to sell than Furricchia and would become richer than she.

She sold some quickly and thought she'd hatch the others to get chickens to sell. But as the hours went by she got thinner and smaller and changed in other ways as well. Soon she had changed into a hen! All day she sat and hatched eggs, but these turned into mice that ran away all over the town. That was what the evil woman had to pay for worshiping envy, jealousy, and greed.

Wise Padre Ulivo

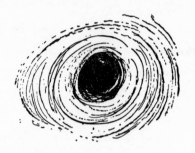

There once lived a man in Italy named Padre Ulivo, who was a wise man. He ate well, drank well, prayed to the Lord, was kind to everyone, and was forever joking and laughing.

But as things go, one day he found he had little to eat or to drink. Between himself and his friends, the cupboard was bare and the bottle was empty. One night there was only a small piece of bread left and just a sip of sour wine. Just the same, he was cheerful and went to sleep with a clear mind. As his head touched the pillow there was a knocking at the door. He got up and opened it, and there stood twelve men, with one at the head of the group.

Said the head man in a kind voice, "Won't you give us something to eat and drink and a lodging for the night?"

"Alas, I have just one small piece of bread and a little thin sour wine in the house."

Replied the head man: "Don't worry about that. Just go to the cupboard and you will find enough good bread. Then go to the cellar and you will find the barrel full of wine."

The men came in and sat down at the table. Padre Ulivo went to the cupboard and there he saw a miracle! The cupboard was full of fine white bread and cornbread. Padre Ulivo opened his eyes wide and his mouth wider, but he believed that when the Lord blesses you, you should be thankful in your heart and say nothing with your mouth. He took the bread and set it before the company.

Then he went to the cellar and there was another miracle! The barrel was full of rich red wine. Padre Ulivo drank with his eyes and rejoiced in his heart and thanked the good Lord for being so kind to him. He brought up the wine and sat down at the table with the men.

They ate well and drank heartily and sang good songs in loud voices. Then Padre Ulivo spread straw on the ground and they went to sleep.

The next morning they arose, thanked Padre Ulivo for his hospitality, and set off on the road. Padre Ulivo liked them so much that he went a way with them. He who was the lord of the company walked at the head, and the others followed. Padre Ulivo walked with the last man.

Said this last one to Padre Ulivo: "He who walks at the head is the Lord of all of us, and anything you wish He can grant. Why don't you go to Him and ask for something?" Padre Ulivo listened carefully, for he had already suspected he was in the presence of one who can do anything. He went to Him as He was walking silently in front of all the others and said:

"Lord, may I ask you a favor?"

"Yes, you may."

"I wish, Lord, that anyone who sits in the big chair in my house will not be able to get out of it until I pull him up."

"It will be exactly as you wish."

Padre Ulivo went back to the last man, with whom he had been talking.

"What did you ask for?" the man said.

Padre Ulivo told him.

"That was not very wise. Why didn't you ask for something worth while? You should go back and ask again. He is generous and will grant you your wish."

Padre Ulivo ran up to the front where He was walking.

"Lord," he said, "would you do me another favor?"

"Yes. What do you want?"

"I would wish that anyone who climbs my fig tree in the orchard will not be able to come down unless I help him down."

"It will be exactly as you desire it."

Padre Ulivo ran back joyfully to the man with whom he had been walking.

"What did you ask for this time?"

"I asked that anyone who climbs my fig tree cannot come down unless I help him down."

"Now, wasn't that a stupid thing to ask? Why didn't you ask to go to Paradise or some other worth-while thing? Go back. You have one more chance. And this time use your head and ask for something of account."

141

Padre Ulivo ran to the front as quickly as his legs would carry him and said, "Will you, Lord, do me one more favor?"

"What is it you desire?"

"I want," said Padre Ulivo slowly, "to be able to beat anyone in the world at cards."

"Your wish is granted," He said.

Padre Ulivo returned to his companion at the end, smiling happily.

"And what did you ask for this time, Padre Ulivo? I hope it was for something good."

"Good indeed it was, brother. I asked to be the winner at cards, no matter with whom I play."

"That was stupid," said the man. "And what is worse, you cannot ask for anything more."

"I don't want anything more," cried Padre Ulivo, "and I don't need anything more. Good-by, good friend, and may you find as much fortune as I have," and he turned home.

From then on Padre Ulivo led a happy and merry life. He had plenty of money and plenty of friends, and never turned anyone from his table or door. So it went on for many years. One day there was a knock at his door. He opened it and there stood Death.

"I've come for you, Padre Ulivo. Your time is up."

"So it is, I guess, and I am ready. Won't you come in and sit down for a few minutes? I just want to straighten up a few things."

Death entered the room.

"Sit down, good friend. There, in that fine chair. It will take me only a few minutes."

Death sat down in the cool room. Pretty soon Padre Ulivo said he was ready. Death tried to get up from the chair—but he couldn't. He tried again and again, but it was no use.

"How can I get up from here?" he cried.

"Only if I help you, good friend. And I will only help you if you let me stay on this good earth with my friends another hundred years."

"Well, you can have another hundred years, but get me up from here."

So Padre Ulivo helped him. Death went off and the good padre lived another hundred years happily and in Christian charity. He never even noticed the time. But one day, when he was in his garden, Death came along the path.

"Padre Ulivo, this time you come, and I don't sit in that chair," said Death.

"Gladly, gladly, friend," Padre Ulivo said, chewing on a juicy ripe fig and picking up his tools.

"What are you eating?" asked Death.

"The finest figs I have ever eaten in my life."

"May I have some?"

"Surely, only I have none left. Why don't you pick some from the tree? I'd get them for you, but I am a little too old, as you well know, to climb trees. Climb up and get some yourself."

Death climbed up quickly, ate juicy figs until he could eat no more, and then began climbing down. But no matter how he tried, he could not get down. The branches held him like a vise.

"Help! Help!" he cried. "How can I get down from this accursed tree?"

"Only if I help you," Padre Ulivo said sweetly. "But if I help you, I want another hundred years of living."

"You can have it, you can have it, only help me down."

Padre Ulivo did, and Death went off in boiling anger.

Padre Ulivo lived another merry hundred years, and then Death was at the door again.

144

"You come with me this time, and I won't sit on chairs or climb trees, either," Death said.

"I am ready, friend Death. I have had enough on this earth. Let us start right now."

So the two went on down the curving, dusty road.

Along came the Devil with hoofs and horns.

"Oho," he cried. "I see you're going to the other world at last."

"I am," said Padre Ulivo, "but it's hot and dusty. Why don't we rest a bit and have a little card game?"

"I don't mind," the Devil said. "What'll we play for?"

"Let's play for souls. You torture so many down in your place."

"Agreed."

They all sat down and began to play. Padre Ulivo won every game. After each game a suffering soul appeared behind him. That made the Devil angry. He jumped up and shouted, "I won't play with you," and ran off.

Death, Padre Ulivo, and the souls came to the gates of Heaven. There Death left them. Padre Ulivo looked at Saint Peter and thought he had seen him before.

145

"What do you want?" asked the saint.

"I want to come in. I have led a good life."

"What is your name?"

"Padre Ulivo."

"And who are those souls behind you?"

"Those I won—I mean, snatched—from the jaws of Satan. I want them to come in with me. They are my friends."

Saint Peter entered and soon came out smiling and said, "The Lord said you may come in, but you may not bring your friends."

Padre Ulivo looked sharply at the saint and said, "Go back to the Lord and tell Him that when He came to my house with His friends, I let them all in. Now I am here with my friends."

Saint Peter smiled in a friendly fashion, went in, and soon came out.

"The Lord says you may all come in," he said, and there was a broad smile on his round face.

So they all went into Heaven and stayed there forever.

The Love of Saint Francis

This tale was told to me by a Franciscan Brother when I was spending heavenly days in Assisi, the city where the *Poverello,* the Little Poor Man Francis, lived and died.

Francis, the true brother of the poor and the sick, had a little fishpond near his convent. It was full of gold and brown-white fish swimming the long day in peaceful pleasure. He loved the creatures in the water as he loved the creatures on the land and in the air—the birds and the beasts, the creeping insects and the flying ones. Each day he came to the little pond to see that no harm came to those living in it.

At the sight of the Little Brother, the fish would swim up in a whirlpool, their mouths wide open. They ate the crumbs he gave them and spoke words of thanks in fish language that Francis understood. He answered and told them how much he loved them, for they were God's creatures.

Now, there were some mean men in Assisi who thought they would play a cruel jest on the godly Little Brother. In those early days some did not favor Francis; they did not understand him.

So, in the dark of the night, they went to the little pond and caught the innocent fish.

The next morning they fried them over a red-hot fire, put them into green leaves, and took them to the little convent in the woods.

"Buon giorno, buona gente [good morning, good people]," Francis greeted them, smiling sweetly and lovingly.

"Good morning, Little Brother, we bring you fine fried fish to eat." And they gave him the fish wrapped in the green leaves.

He looked at the men with his kind brown eyes, smiled gently, and thanked them, saying, "May the sweet Lord bless you and take care of you, *amici* [friends]."

They went away feeling a little guilty, but laughing just the same at what they thought was a great joke on Francis. Now he would eat the creatures he loved!

Francis stood still, holding the brown fish in his hands; then he spoke softly:

"Little fish, forgive these cruel men, they did not know what they were doing. I love you even as the Lord loves you in His infinite pity, and I pray to the Lord to bring you back to life so you can be happy in the water again." Then he went to the pond and dropped the fish into the water, and lo, a miracle! The fish became alive and swam off gaily. Francis sang out, "The sweet Lord can do anything in His loving kindness."

When the mean men in Assisi heard of the wondrous miracle, they said they would never again do anything unkind to Francis or anyone else. Some of them were so changed that they even joined the brotherhood.

A Few Notes
about the Stories

Since this is, first and last, a book of stories to be read and told with pleasure, long, scholarly discussions of the origins, history, and recurrence of the tales would be out of place. However, here are a few words about each one that will give you an inkling of the rich study behind them, if you desire to go into it.

If this research work interests you, you will find the books* by Professor Antti Aarne and Stith Thompson of enormous value.

Here are short notes on each of the stories.

(1) FISH ALIVE! When you go to Siena, as I have done many times, you will, of course, visit the Cathedral, and there you will see, among many works of beauty, the floor mosaics of Domenico Beccafumi. The guide, if you have one, or a native of the town will tell you about Beccafumi as a boy, as a man, and as an artist. And you probably will be told the well-known story you read here. Naturally, Miss Guerrini knew of it and gave it to me.

Sometimes you may read it or hear it told a little differently from the way I tell it. But remember each storyteller

---

* *The Types of the Folk-Tale,* by Antti Aarne, edited and enlarged by Stith Thompson. Also *Motif-Index of Folk-Literature,* by Stith Thompson.

tells a story in his or her own way. There is no harm in this
if the original theme of the story is not changed.

(2) THE MIRACLE OF THE ROSE. Lady Paula, of whom
this tale is told, really lived many years ago. Her name was
Paula Gambara Costa de Benevagienna. She lived in the
castle of Bene in the province of Cuneo. This miraculous
story is well known thereabouts, both by word of mouth
and in books. Miss Guerrini and Miss Mosiici both con-
tributed this tale.

Other lands have similar stories; the most famous one is
found in Hungary, where it is told about Saint Elizabeth.

(3) KING CLOTHES. I heard the "Giufa" stories for the
first time in a perfect setting for such tales—in a restaurant
filled with the good, sharp smells of food, and noisy with
friendly laughter. It was on a hot July evening in uptown
"Little Italy" in New York City. Outside, the sidewalks were
packed with young and old—a holiday crowd. The curbs
of the sidewalks were lined with pushcarts decked with flar-
ing torches and sharp electric lights, and loaded with fruits,
candies, nuts, sizzling sausages garnished with green-red
peppers, white and brown onions and potatoes—all making
a marvelous painting. Other pushcarts held many-colored
toys, dolls, and waxen-white candles of every size, decorated
with delicate golden-green designs. The whole scene was a
milling, shouting, gay celebration in honor of Our Lady of
Carmel. The Heavenly Host, pleasure, and prayer generally
go hand in hand with Italians.

At the table next to me sat a short fat man with a bulbous
nose and a barrelly stomach. He roared with booming laughter at every word, and shouted and ate loudly. I liked that
combination of Cyrano and Gargantua the moment I saw
him, and I was quick to tell him what I wanted: to wit,
stories. As usual, I began by telling some. He laughed up-

roariously at every word. Others in the room also became interested. I told some tall tales, and he came back with Giufa tales. Though his English was crotchety, Salvatore Costello, dealer in fine-smelling cheeses and crisp Italian bread, was a natural storyteller. Words poured pell-mell out of him, and I heard many tales. Some of these stories I heard again from my shoe-repair man, Frank Son,* and from other Italians who had come from Sicily, for Giufa is one of the well-known folk-hero-clowns of Sicily.

There is a cycle of stories about Giufa, the silly-wise peasant, as there is about Tyll Ulenspiegel, the merry Flemish prankster,† and the Merry Men of Gotham† in England. Giufa tales are found in many parts of Italy. Sometimes his name is slightly changed; thus in Tuscany and Rome it is spelled Giucca.

The tale of Giufa and his clothes is also told of Dante. It is found in the *Arabian Nights,* too.

(4) THE LUCKY DOG. Miss Guerrini heard this tale— and so did I—in Verona. It was told to me by someone who had lived there all his life.

We were walking home after a performance of *Romeo and Juliet.* "You are a lucky dog to see such a performance every year," I said. "It is the only city where this play should be seen."

"Lucky dog! That makes me think of a story that's told around here. You are always asking me for stories, so here is one. It comes from Piedmont, I believe."

* When I asked Frank what his Italian name was, he said: "Frank Son."

"What is your father's name?" I asked. He looked at me for a time and then said, "Giovanni Son." So Son it is.

† See *Tyll Ulenspiegel's Merry Pranks* and *The Merry Men of Gotham.* Vanguard Press, New York.

It was the same story Miss Guerrini had given me, except for the proverb at the end. Treasure-finding with the help of dreams is as old as the Bible, and there have been stories about this kind of good fortune in every land in the world.

(5) CHIROLA AND THE BLACK OLD MAN. This story is a strange mixture of various fragments of stories. The Devil behaves here quite unusually, and the goat part comes from black-believing Germany.

Around Florence, the Devil often conducts himself somewhat differently than he does in other places. Sometimes he is very friendly and familiar, and sometimes he lives up to his name.

Miss Guerrini and Miss Mosiici, who have lived almost all their lives in Florence, have come across many Florence Devil tales, among them this one. It is known both orally and in written forms in collections of Italian folk tales.

(6) THE PRICELESS CATS. This, of course, is the old Dick Whittington story with a fresh and new surprise ending— an ending that gives it a delightfully satirical turn that adds a pleasant interest to an old theme. I heard it many years ago in Perugia. The new ending of the story is undoubtedly a later addition, but then, folk stories change like clouds in the sky.

(7) THE HAND OF THE LORD and (12) A MIRACLE OF A SAINT. Once some trouble with my eyes brought me to a doctor who had a charming brown-eyed nurse with a complexion of "summer giggling through the rounded trees." We started to talk, and the talking resulted, as it always does, in folk stories.

Miss Helen Rossi (that was the nurse's name) has a father, Joseph Rossi, who is now seventy-six years old. He was born in Salerno, in Italy, where he heard stories from his parents that he later told to his own children, and he hopes they

153

will pass them on to *their* children. "Pop" Rossi's tales were local religious ones "that everybody around Salerno knows and tells."

(8) A LONG, LONG NIGHT and (10) EAT AND LIKE IT. Noodle stories—comic stories dealing with the customs and habits of people living in a particular town—are found in every country in the world, including our own. Near Siena, in the central part of Italy, is the town of Montieri, whose people have been chosen as the victims of good-natured banter. In a sense, these tales are similar to those of the Merry Men of Gotham and to others of this type throughout the world.

Miss Guerrini had both heard and read these stories, and gave them to me. I also heard some of them in Little Italy in New York from various sources. These stories have a familiar ring, of course, but they are so amusing and so descriptive of the land that they are well worth telling.

(9) NICOLA PESCE. Sicily has sent more Italians to New York than any other region of Italy, and so the story of Nicola Pesce, one of Sicily's folk heroes, is quite well known here. Miss Guerrini first told me the story, and later I heard it again from three different Italians in New York. The versions differed slightly: in two of them the princess loved the diver and pleaded with her father for him.

This is an heroic legend in which the poor—the common man—is the hero and the king is heartless. The word *pesce* means "fish," and so the very name indicates Nicola Pesce's kinship with the sea.

(11) A FLOWER FOR A HUSBAND! Florence is filled with beautiful art and fine stories, and this tale is well known. I heard it years ago on one of my visits. I am sure it is to be found in books, but I have not seen it.

The number "three," as a symbolic number, is common

in fairy tales, and the flower theme is an ancient one. This story illustrates the personal and friendly way in which witches behave in Italy. This is quite unlike many other countries such as Germany, where a witch is everything ugly and horrible. Of course, there are terrible witches in Italy, too, but they aren't so prominent as they are in other lands.

(13) THE SUN WILL ALWAYS SHINE.   I heard this story first in Venice in 1951 from a young fellow by the name of Gino Stella. He was guiding (not professionally) some Americans through the marvelous city on the sea. We met in the Palazzo Ducale (Doges' Palace), and the regular guide had taken us all down to the *pozzi,* the dank, greasy dungeons used by the Doges in the olden days for inflicting their savage punishments. When we came into the living sunlight on the Piazza San Marco, with its holiday crowd, Gino said he would tell us a tale to take away the sickening dungeon taste—and this was the tale.

It was a well-known story in Venice, he said, and later I learned that the same story is told about Dante and Cecco d'Ascoli, Dante being the man who thinks he can perform the miracle.

(14) WISE WORDS WITH GOLDEN PROFIT.   I heard this story twenty-six years ago from one of the guides in the Pitti Palace with whom I had become quite friendly. There are endless tales in Italy about their great artists and craftsmen. Many of them are told to this very day by men who work in the palaces that have now become art galleries. This story is unquestionably recorded in some old, old volume telling of the lives of Italian craftsmen and artists.

Niccolò Grosso was known as an eccentric man in his day, and the story is not unlike the man. He was also known as "Il Caparra" * because he never kept any accounts, and

* A man who demands payment in advance.

people jestingly said he would burn his accounting books and demand his pay before he would begin any work.

(15) THE LOST PARADISE. Stories about the inquisitiveness of women are as old as woman, and there are tales of this type in every part of the world. Generally it is the woman who creates the trouble. This story was told to me in Rome by a gentleman named Paniconi, who had a small store in Trieste and who was in the capital for a visit.

Later I heard the story again in New York City, and I am sure it can be found in every other city in the world, for it is a tale that began with Eve in Paradise. The "bird" incident is also very common.

A *terrina* is a tall earthen dish with a cover.

(16) A LESSON WELL LEARNED. One lovely morning in Padua in 1951 I was sitting with a student, Giovanni Garibaldi, eating wild strawberries and watching a parade with rolling banners and martial music. He knew I was in search of folk stories and told me this one.

Stories of punishing pride are common in every land, beginning with India, where many stories are said to have originated. There is a similar story told in green Ireland about Saint Eloi, a goldsmith by trade, and the way in which he was punished for the sin of pride. As usual, the versions vary a little.

(17) THE WISDOM OF CECCHINO. According to Miss Guerrini and Miss Mosiici, who gave me this tale, it is one that is well known in the province of Puglia. The same theme can also be found in other lands. It follows the fairy-tale formula of the three sons, one of whom is either seemingly lazy or seemingly stupid and who proves the wisest and most successful in the end. The only country where such stories are not found is in America. When they do crop up, they are always stories adopted from other lands.

(18) WHY DONKEYS HAVE LONG EARS. This story is quite common in Sicily. I heard it from Mr. Costello during the fiesta of Our Lady of Carmel.

"Why" stories are known throughout the world, not only about animals, but also about flowers, birds, and every other kind of creature, including human beings. We have many of them in America.

One of the interesting points about this tale is that it shows the friendly familiarity between the Holy Lord and animals. The same personal relationship exists between Italian people and the Lord—a relationship that found its most beautiful expression in the acts and beliefs of Saint Francis of Assisi.

(19) RED FLOWERS IN WHITE SNOW. This story was told by Signore Uguccione Ranieri di Sorbello, of Perugia, so it is probably well known in the province of Umbria. Miss Guerrini heard it from her father.

Rewarding the unselfish, and removing a physical defect, particularly a growth on the back (or adding one, as a punishment), is a theme that has gone around the whole world.

(20) THE STORY OF THE STONE HEN. Such a tale could originate only among everyday folk who sell eggs. There is nothing literary about it. It is a fairly recent Florentine story, probably about two or three hundred years old.

I heard it in Perugia in 1934 from a man by the name of Guardabasi. My notes read: "Sitting in open-air garden. Summer-session students of University dancing." My informant said that the story is in a book, but he was told it one time when he was visiting his relatives in Florence.

The egg-laying part is very common in fairy tales, but the application to modern life is unique. The odd mixture of the pagan, the religious, and the modern is unusual.

(21) WISE PADRE ULIVO. Salvatore Costello, who liked

good, healthy, ribald tales best of all, told me this one. Here again is an example of the homey, friendly attitude of the Italians toward the Holy Lord, saints, and priests.

Italians worship and revere the Lord, but they also look upon Him as a guiding father and as a personal friend, even to the point of criticism and argument. This attitude adds a human charm to the tale. This story is also called "Pret Olivo." It is found in many regions of Italy as well as in other parts of Europe.

(22) THE LOVE OF SAINT FRANCIS. No book of Italian folk stories is complete without a tale of the most godly human being who ever lived during the past two thousand years: Saint Francis of Assisi.

I spent one full summer and many other short visits in Assisi and in different Umbrian hill towns where Francis performed his holy work. There I heard many beautiful stories about the Little Poor Brother—this one among them. It was told to me by an English Franciscan monk who was there for study. The keeper of the inn where I stayed also knew the tale.

Most convents had small *pescherias*—fishponds or fish tanks where fish were kept fresh for the table. *Pescheria* also means "fish market," but not when used in the sense of this tale.